Consultant: Ann Bobker

Copyright © 2001 **Popular Book Company (Canada) Limited**

Printed in China

Contents

Section I

	Overview	5
1.	Comparing Sizes	6
2.	Comparing Heights and Lengths	10
3.	Comparing Shapes and Weights	12
4.	Comparing Positions	16
5.	Matching and Arranging Objects	20
	Midway Review	24
6.	Ordering Objects (1)	28
7.	Ordering Objects (2)	30
8.	Sorting Objects (1)	34
9.	Sorting Objects (2)	38
	Final Review	42

Section II

	Overview	47
1.	Addition and Subtraction of 1	48
2.	Addition Facts to 6	52
3.	Subtraction Facts to 6	56
4.	Addition and Subtraction of 0	60
5.	Addition and Subtraction Facts to 6	64
6.	Addition Facts to 10	68
7.	Subtraction Facts to 10	72
8.	Addition and Subtracton Facts to 10	76
	Midway Review	80
9.	Addition Facts to 15	84
10.	Subtraction Facts to 15	88
11.	Addition and Subtraction Facts to 15	92
12.	Addition Facts to 20	96
13.	Subtraction Facts to 20	100
14.	Addition and Subtraction Facts to 20	104
15.	More Addition and Subtraction	108
16.	Addition and Subtraction with Money	112
	Final Review	116

Section III

	Overview	121
1.	Comparing, Sorting and Ordering	122
2.	Numbers 1-10	126
3.	Addition and Subtraction	130

4. Numbers 11-20 134

5. Shapes 140

6. Solid Column Graphs 142

7. Numbers 20-100 146

Midway Test 152

8. More about Addition and Subtraction 158

9. Measurement 164

10. Time 170

11. Money 174

12. Shapes 178

13. Pictographs 182

Final Test 186

Section IV

Overview 193

1. Numbers 1 to 10 194

2. Addition and Subtraction to 10 196

3. Addition and Subtraction to 20 200

4. Shapes 204

5. Solid Column Graphs 208

Midway Review 212

6. Numbers 20 to 100 216

7. Addition and Subtraction to 50 220

8. Addition and Subtraction to 100 224

9. Money 228

10. Measurement 232

11. Pictographs 234

12. Probability 238

Final Review 240

Parents' Guide 245
Answers 249

Section 1

Overview

In this section, Grade 1 students are provided with practice in comparing, sorting and ordering objects according to one attribute such as size, height, width and weight.

They will be colouring and copying objects as well as copying or choosing between words that describe objects, such as heavier/lighter and biggest/smallest. Minimal reading and writing skills are required.

Parents can enrich children's learning by providing them with real objects or drawings for comparing, sorting and ordering, which help to arouse and sustain their interest in exploring and learning mathematics.

Comparing Sizes

Circle the smaller object.

Circle the bigger animal.

Draw a similar shape which is bigger than the one shown.

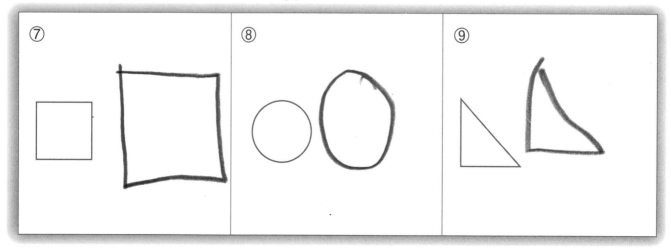

Colour the container which holds more juice.

Draw a similar snack which is smaller than the one shown.

Colour the biggest fruit.

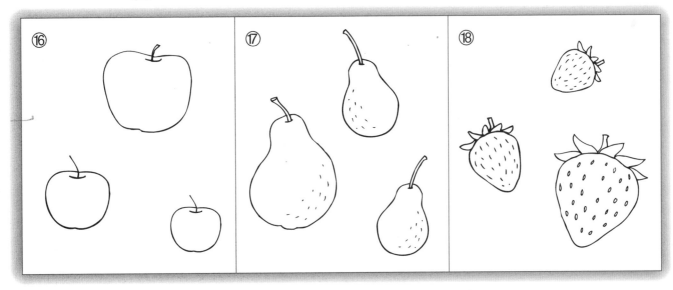

Colour the smallest animal.

Colour the container with the least water.

Draw lines to join the bears to their chairs.

Circle the correct word in each sentence.

㉘ 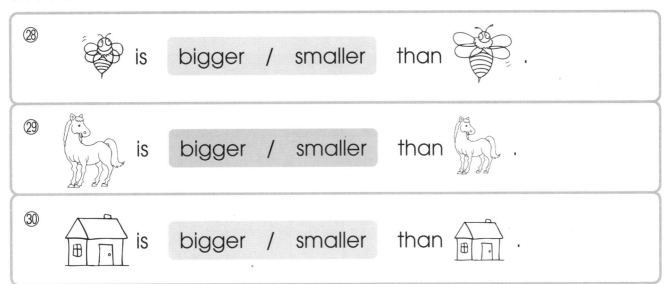 is **bigger / smaller** than 🐝 .

㉙ 🐎 is **bigger / smaller** than 🐴 .

㉚ 🏠 is **bigger / smaller** than 🏠 .

Look at the gift boxes. Circle the correct word in each sentence.

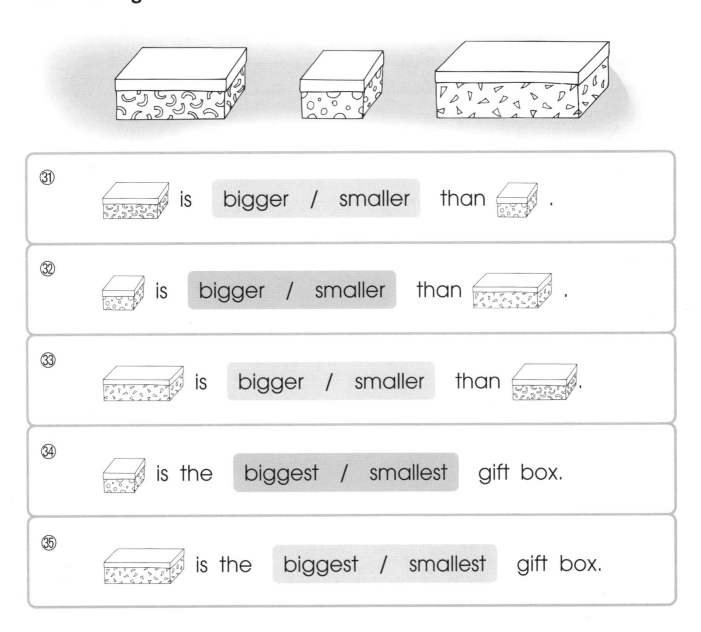

㉛ is **bigger / smaller** than .

㉜ is **bigger / smaller** than .

㉝ is **bigger / smaller** than .

㉞ is the **biggest / smallest** gift box.

㉟ is the **biggest / smallest** gift box.

Comparing Heights and Lengths

Colour the longer sausage.

Colour the shortest pencil.

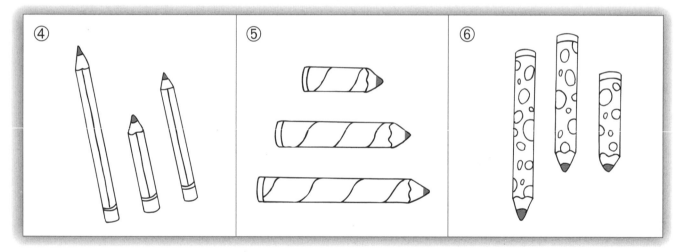

Draw a similar object which is longer than the one shown.

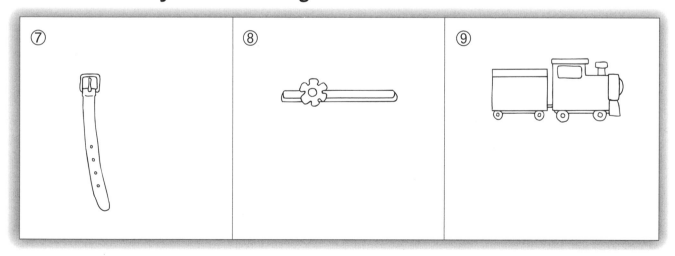

Draw a line which is as long as the one given.

Colour the taller child.

Colour the tallest one.

Draw a similar object which is as tall as the one given.

Comparing Shapes and Weights

Colour the correct answers.

① Colour the bread which has the thickest slices.

② Colour the bottle which has the widest neck.

③ Colour the sharpest pencil.

④ Colour the house which has the widest pathway green and the house which has the narrowest window blue.

⑤ Colour the thing which is flat.

⑥ Colour the thing which is hollow.

⑦ Colour the thinnest book.

⑧ Colour the widest shape.

⑨ Colour the heaviest fruit.

⑩ Colour the lightest stationery.

Colour the heavier box.

Check ✔ the correct balances.

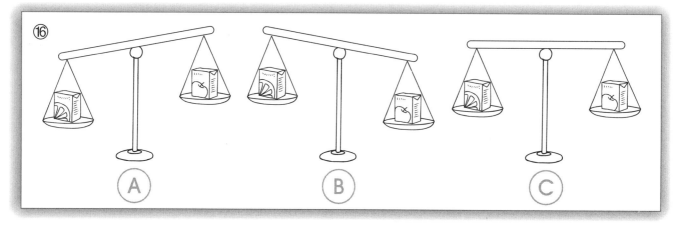

Look at the balances. Draw a picture to complete each sentence.

⑰   🍐   is lighter than   ☐ .

⑱   🍐   is as heavy as   ☐ .

⑲   🍌   is lighter than   ☐ .

⑳   ☐   is the heaviest fruit.

Look at the pictures. Circle the correct word in each sentence.

㉑ The 👦 is lighter / heavier

than the 👧 .

㉒ The 👧 is lighter / heavier

than the 👦 .

㉓ The 🍵 is lighter / heavier

than the 🍴 .

㉔ The 🔩 is lighter / heavier

than the 🍴 .

Circle the correct word in each sentence.

㉕ The opposite of light is lighter / heavy .

㉖ The opposite of heavier is lighter / heavy .

Comparing Positions

Circle the correct words.

① 🐱 is on / under the 🪑 .

② 🎁 is on / under the 🪑 .

③ Katie has a 🎈 in her left / right hand.

④ Katie has a 🍭 in her left / right hand.

⑤ Eva is standing on Katie's left / right .

⑥ Kevin is standing in front of / behind Katie.

⑦ 🎂 is in front of / behind Katie.

⑧ 🥄 is inside / outside the 🥣 .

⑨ 🥢 are inside / outside the 🥤 .

Write 'left' or 'right' to complete each sentence.

⑩ holds the with her _____ hand.

⑪ 's leash is in 's _____ hand.

⑫ The are on 's _____ .

⑬ is on 's _____ .

Write 'in front of' or 'behind' to complete each sentence.

⑭ There is a standing _____ the .

⑮ There are some standing _____ the .

⑯ The is standing _____ the .

Write 'over' or 'under' to complete each sentence.

⑰ The is jumping _____ the .

⑱ The is standing _____ the .

⑲ The is flying _____ the .

⑳ Two are _____ the .

Colour the pictures. Then write the correct words.

㉑ Colour the 🧸 that is inside the 📦 brown.

㉒ Colour the 🪆 that is outside the 📦 green.

㉓ 🤖 is _____ the box.

㉔ Colour the 👦 that is under the ⛱ yellow.

㉕ Colour the 🧺 that is under the 🪑 red.

㉖ The 🐦 is flying _____ the ⛱ .

㉗ Colour the 👦 that is standing in front of the 🌳 blue.

㉘ Colour the 👧 that is standing behind the 🌳 orange.

㉙ The 🐶 is _____ the 🐱 .

18   COMPLETE MATHSMART (GRADE 1)

Draw the pictures.

㉚ Draw a 🍭 in Sam's right hand.

㉛ Draw a ✏️ in Sam's left hand.

㉜ Draw a ⚽ inside the 📦.

㉝ Draw a 🎾 outside the 📦.

㉞ Draw an 🍎 outside the 🥣.

㉟ Draw a 🍌 inside the 🥣.

㊱ Draw a ⚽ under the 🪑.

㊲ Draw a 🕊️ flying over the 🏠.

㊳ Draw some 🌸 in front of the 🏠.

㊴ Draw a 🌳 on the left of the 🏠.

Matching and Arranging Objects

Write the correct word to complete each sentence.

Apples   Pears   Orange   Peaches

① There are more apples than _____ .

② There are fewer apples than _____ .

③ There are more pears than _____ .

④ There are as many apples as _____ .

Look at the stickers. Draw the pictures to complete the sentences.

⑤ There are more ◯ than 🌷 .

⑥ There are fewer ◯ than 🌷 .

⑦ There are more ◯ than ❀ .

⑧ There are fewer ◯ than ✿ .

Look at the pictures. Put a check mark ✔ in the correct circle to complete each sentence.

⑨ There are more 🪏 than ◯ ⭐ ◯ 🪣 ◯ 🐚 .

⑩ There are fewer 🪣 than ◯ ⭐ ◯ 🪏 ◯ 🐚 .

⑪ If Joe takes 1 🪏 away, there are as many 🪏 as

◯ ⭐ ◯ 🪏 ◯ 🐚 .

Look at Joe's balloons. Circle the correct word to complete each sentence.

⑫ There are more / fewer 🎈 than 🎈 .

⑬ There are more / fewer 🎈 than 🎈 .

⑭ There are more / fewer 🎈 than 🎈 .

Put each group in order. Write the letters only.

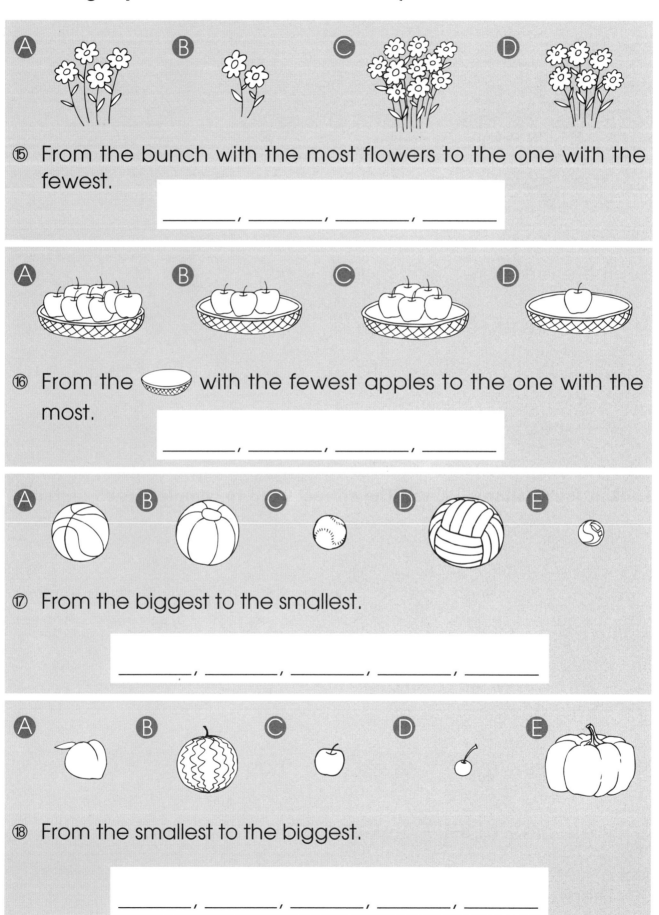

⑮ From the bunch with the most flowers to the one with the fewest.

_____ , _____ , _____ , _____

⑯ From the 🥣 with the fewest apples to the one with the most.

_____ , _____ , _____ , _____

⑰ From the biggest to the smallest.

_____ , _____ , _____ , _____ , _____

⑱ From the smallest to the biggest.

_____ , _____ , _____ , _____ , _____

Look at Jill's cookies. Circle the correct word or letter to complete each sentence. Then draw the pictures.

Ⓐ   Ⓑ   Ⓒ

⑲ Cookie A is smaller / bigger than cookie C.

⑳ Cookie B is smaller / bigger than cookie A.

㉑ Cookie A / B / C is the biggest.

㉒ Cookie A / B / C is the smallest.

㉓ Put the cookies in order from the biggest to the smallest.

㉔ Draw a cookie that is bigger than cookie B and with more chocolate chips on top.

㉕ Draw a cookie that is smaller than cookie A and with fewer chocolate chips on top.

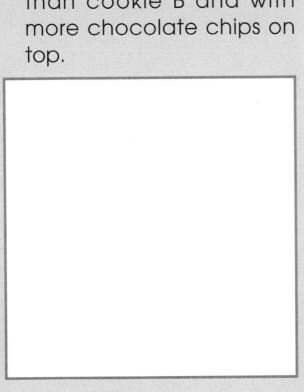

Midway

Colour the things. Then write the letters to put them in order.

 A   B   C   D

①   a.   Colour the biggest fruit yellow and the smallest red.

     b.   From the biggest to the smallest: ____ , ____ , ____ , ____

 A   B   C   D

②   a.   Colour the container that holds the most water green and the one that holds the least blue.

     b.   From the one that holds the most water to the one that holds the least: ____ , ____ , ____ , ____

Draw the pictures.

③ Draw a ✏ which is longer than the one shown.

④ Draw a 🚪 which is narrower than the one shown.

⑤ Draw a which is taller than the one shown.

⑥ Draw a which is thinner than the one shown.

Circle the correct words.

⑦ Jack is standing in front of / behind Lucy.

⑧ Katie is standing on Lucy's left / right .

⑨ Jack is holding a towel with his left / right hand.

⑩ The carpet is over / under the box.

⑪ The dolls are inside / outside the box.

⑫ The robot is bigger / smaller than the doll.

⑬ There are more / fewer dolls than robots.

Check ✓ the heavier object.

Fill in the blanks.

⑱ Jack is holding a 🍭 with his _____ left/right hand.

⑲ Betsy is holding a 🍴 with her _____ left/right hand.

⑳ Betsy is sitting on the _____ left/right of Brad.

㉑ Sally is standing _____ behind/in front of Brad.

㉒ Anne is putting a 🍽 _____ over/under Jack's head.

㉓ The 🥄 is _____ inside/outside the 🥧 .

㉔ The 🎉 is _____ inside/outside the 🎁 .

Check ✔ the group which has more.

㉕ Ⓐ Ⓑ

㉖ Ⓐ Ⓑ

㉗ Ⓐ Ⓑ

㉘ Ⓐ Ⓑ

Match the muffins with the boxes. Then fill in the blanks with the correct letters.

㉚ Group _____ has the most 🧁 .

㉛ Group _____ has the fewest 🧁 .

㉜ Put the groups in order from the one which has the most 🧁 to the one which has the least.

_____ , _____ , _____

Ordering Objects (1)

Cross out X the thing in each group which is in the wrong order.

Draw lines to match the animals with their food by size.

Match the things with the correct boxes. Write the letters in the circles.

Ordering Objects (2)

Put each group of things in order. Write the letters only.

①

From the longest to the shortest: _____ , _____ , _____ , _____

②

From the thickest to the thinnest: _____ , _____ , _____ , _____

③

From the narrowest to the widest: _____ , _____ , _____ , _____

④

From the tallest to the shortest: _____ , _____ , _____ , _____

⑤

From the smallest to the biggest: _____ , _____ , _____ , _____

⑥

A   B   C   D

From the lightest to the heaviest: _____ , _____ , _____ , _____

⑦

A
B
C
D

From the shortest to the longest: _____ , _____ , _____ , _____

⑧

A   B   C   D

From the group with the most pencils to the one with the fewest: _____ , _____ , _____ , _____

⑨

A   B   C   D

From the container which can hold the most water to the one which can hold the least: _____ , _____ , _____ , _____

⑩

A   B   C   D

From the vase with the least water to the one with the most: _____ , _____ , _____ , _____

Look at the jars and the cookies. Then answer the questions by writing the letters only.

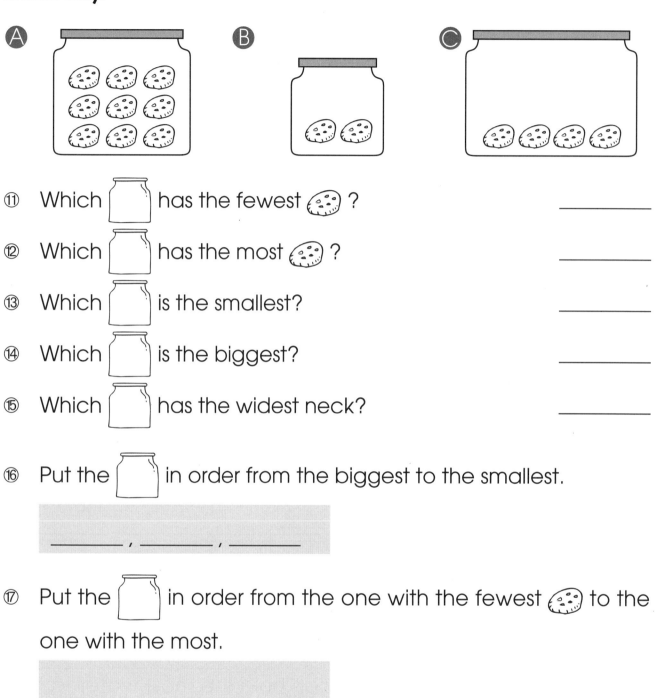

⑪ Which [jar] has the fewest 🍪 ? _____

⑫ Which [jar] has the most 🍪 ? _____

⑬ Which [jar] is the smallest? _____

⑭ Which [jar] is the biggest? _____

⑮ Which [jar] has the widest neck? _____

⑯ Put the [jar] in order from the biggest to the smallest.

_____ , _____ , _____

⑰ Put the [jar] in order from the one with the fewest 🍪 to the one with the most.

_____ , _____ , _____

Colour the jar which is smaller than C and holding fewer cookies than C.

⑱

Look at the baskets of apples. Fill in the blanks and put the baskets in order.

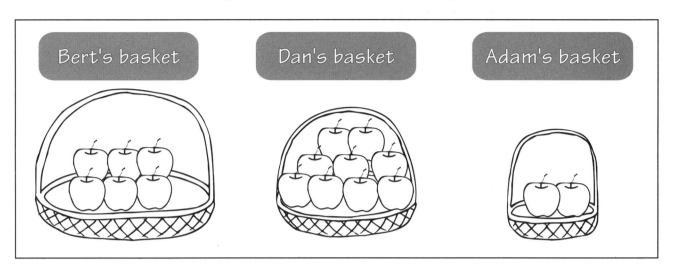

⑲ _____ 's is the biggest.

⑳ _____ 's is the smallest.

㉑ Put the in order from the biggest to the smallest.

_____ 's , _____ 's , _____ 's

㉒ _____ 's has the most 🍎 .

㉓ _____ 's has the fewest 🍎 .

㉔ _____ has more 🍎 than Bert.

㉕ _____ has fewer 🍎 than Bert.

㉖ Put the children in order from the child who has the most 🍎 to the one who has the least.

_____ , _____ , _____

Sorting Objects (1)

Cross out X the one that does not belong.

⑦

⑧

⑨

⑩

⑪

⑫

Cross out X the objects which are in the wrong place.

Draw lines to join the toys to the box and the clothing to the basket.

㉑

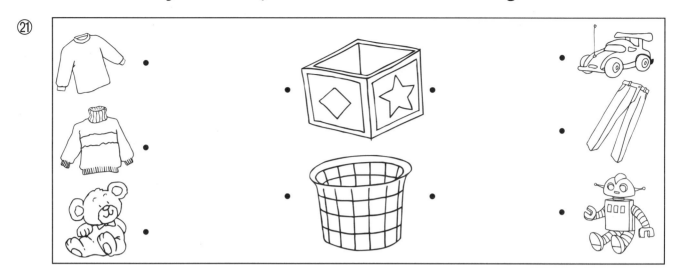

Draw lines to join the letters to the letter box and the numbers to the number box.

㉒

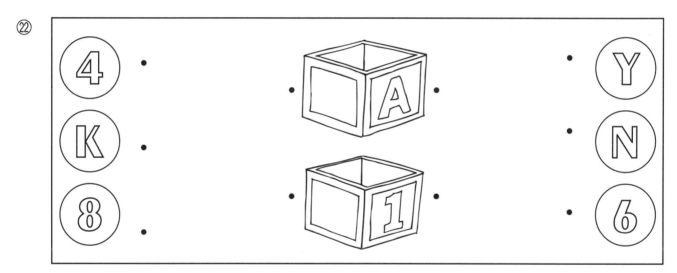

Draw lines to join the tools to the tool box and the cooking utensils to the tray.

㉓

Sorting Objects (2)

Colour the correct pictures.

① Colour the things you might find at a birthday party.

② Colour the animals you would find in water.

③ Colour the things you might find on the beach.

④ Colour the food you would put in the refrigerator.

⑤ Colour the things you would put in the closet.

⑥ Colour the things you would find in a grocery store.

⑦ Colour the things you would find on a farm.

⑧ Colour the things you would drink.

Sort the things. Write the letters in the boxes.

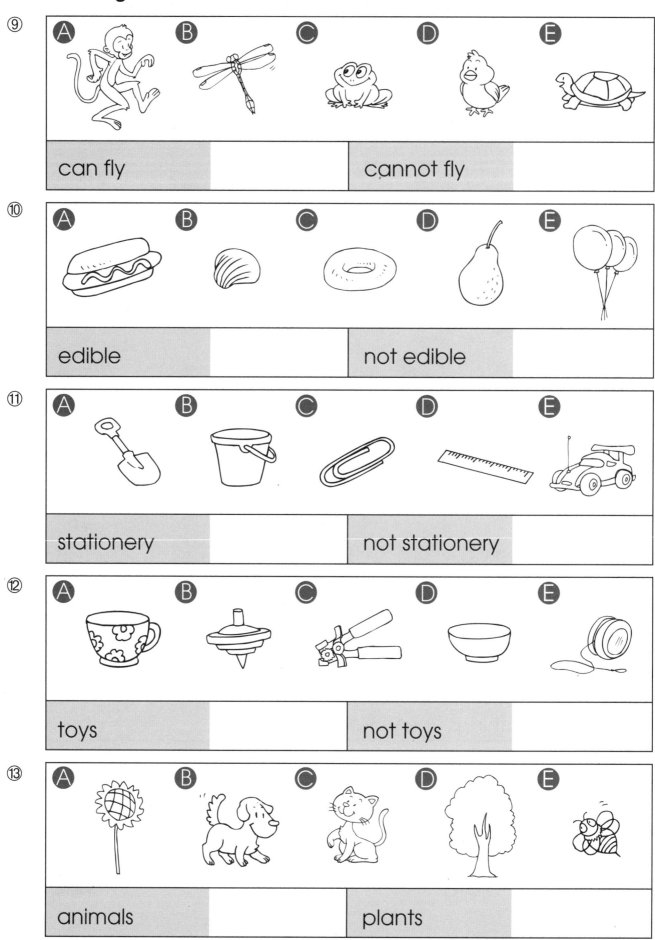

⑨ A B C D E

can fly   cannot fly

⑩ A B C D E

edible   not edible

⑪ A B C D E

stationery   not stationery

⑫ A B C D E

toys   not toys

⑬ A B C D E

animals   plants

Divide the clothing into 3 different groups. Colour each group with the same colour.

⑭

Divide the animals into 2 groups. Colour each group of animals with the same colour.

⑮

Divide the toys into 2 groups. Colour each group of toys with the same colour.

⑯

Colour the thing that does not belong in each group.

①

②

③

④

Cross out ✗ the things that are put in the wrong place.

⑤   ⑥

Colour the ribbons and put them in order.

⑦

a. Colour the longest ribbon blue and the shortest yellow.

b. Put the ribbons in order from the longest to the shortest.

_____ , _____ , _____

Cross out X the thing which is in the wrong order.

⑧

⑨

⑩

Put the things in order. Write the letters.

⑪ Ⓐ Ⓑ Ⓒ | From small to big:

_____ , _____ , _____

⑫ Ⓐ Ⓑ Ⓒ | From thick to thin:

_____ , _____ , _____

⑬ Ⓐ Ⓑ Ⓒ | From light to heavy:

Marshmallow   flour

_____ , _____ , _____

⑭ Ⓐ Ⓑ Ⓒ | From long to short:

_____ , _____ , _____

Draw lines to join the stationery to the pencil case and the toys to the toy box.

⑮
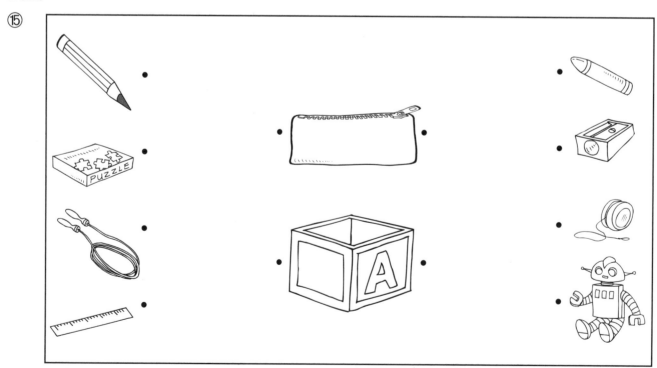

Draw lines to join the things to the correct stores.

⑯

Divide the things into two groups. Colour each group with the same colour.

⑰

⑱

Help the bee reach the flowers by colouring the animals that have wings.

⑲

Which comes next? Circle the correct picture.

⑳

㉑

㉒

㉓

Overview

In Section I, children practised preschool skills such as comparing, sorting and ordering objects according to a single attribute such as size, height and weight. They also matched objects by one-to-one correspondence and practised counting to identify sets with more, fewer, or the same number of objects. These skills are now built upon in Section II.

In this section, children are given exercises to develop and practise the basic arithmetic skills of addition and subtraction.

Addition involves putting two groups together whereas subtraction involves taking one group from another.

Through drawing or using concrete materials, the concept of addition and subtraction is reinforced. Children learn such mathematical terms as sum, difference, total and equal, and also the signs (+, −, =) that represent these terms.

Before children make any number sentences, they must understand the quantities the numbers represent, and what happens when quantities are combined or when two groups are compared.

These skills are applied in everyday situations, using whole numbers up to 20.

Addition and Subtraction of 1

1. → add 1 →

  3   +   1   =   4

2. → subtract 1 →

  3   −   1   =   2

HINTS:

- Adding 1 is to count 1 forward.
- Subtracting 1 is to count 1 backward.
- " + " means ADD.
- " _ " means SUBTRACT.
- " = " means EQUAL TO.

Draw 1 more. How many are there in all?

①   2

②   _____

③ _____   ④ _____

Cross 1 out. How many are left?

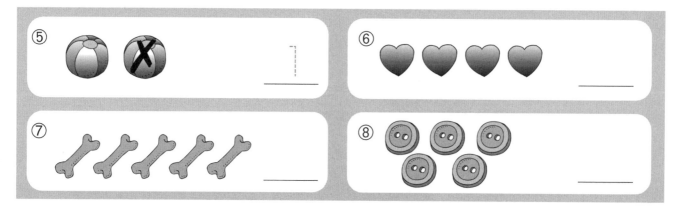

⑤   1

⑥

⑦

⑧

How many are there?

⑨

$$\begin{array}{r} 3 \\ + 1 \\ \hline \end{array}$$
$3 + 1 =$ _____

⑩

$$\begin{array}{r} 4 \\ + 1 \\ \hline \end{array}$$
$4 + 1 =$ _____

⑪

$$\begin{array}{r} 4 \\ - 1 \\ \hline \end{array}$$
$4 - 1 =$ _____

⑫

$$\begin{array}{r} 6 \\ + 1 \\ \hline \end{array}$$
$6 + 1 =$ _____

⑬

$$\begin{array}{r} 2 \\ + 1 \\ \hline \end{array}$$
$2 + 1 =$ _____

⑭

$$\begin{array}{r} 5 \\ - 1 \\ \hline \end{array}$$
$5 - 1 =$ _____

⑮

$$\begin{array}{r} 7 \\ - 1 \\ \hline \end{array}$$
$7 - 1 =$ _____

⑯

$$\begin{array}{r} 3 \\ - 1 \\ \hline \end{array}$$
$3 - 1 =$ _____

⑰

$$\begin{array}{r} 8 \\ + 1 \\ \hline \end{array}$$
$8 + 1 =$ _____

⑱

$$\begin{array}{r} 8 \\ - 1 \\ \hline \end{array}$$
$8 - 1 =$ _____

Add or subtract.

⑲ 1 + 1 = ☐

⑳ 2 - 1 = ☐

㉑ 2 + 1 = ☐

㉒ 3 - 1 = ☐

㉓ 3 + 1 = ☐

㉔ 4 - 1 = ☐

㉕ 4 + 1 = ☐

㉖ 5 - 1 = ☐

㉗ 5 + 1 = ☐

㉘ 6 - 1 = ☐

㉙ 6 + 1 = ☐

㉚ 7 - 1 = ☐

㉛ 7 + 1 = ☐

㉜ 8 - 1 = ☐

㉝
$$\begin{array}{r} 8 \\ + 1 \\ \hline \end{array}$$
☐

㉞
$$\begin{array}{r} 9 \\ + 1 \\ \hline \end{array}$$
☐

㉟
$$\begin{array}{r} 10 \\ - 1 \\ \hline \end{array}$$
☐

㊱
$$\begin{array}{r} 2 \\ + 1 \\ \hline \end{array}$$
☐

㊲
$$\begin{array}{r} 5 \\ + 1 \\ \hline \end{array}$$
☐

㊳
$$\begin{array}{r} 9 \\ - 1 \\ \hline \end{array}$$
☐

㊴
$$\begin{array}{r} 4 \\ + 1 \\ \hline \end{array}$$
☐

㊵
$$\begin{array}{r} 5 \\ - 1 \\ \hline \end{array}$$
☐

㊶
$$\begin{array}{r} 4 \\ - 1 \\ \hline \end{array}$$
☐

㊷
$$\begin{array}{r} 3 \\ + 1 \\ \hline \end{array}$$
☐

㊸
$$\begin{array}{r} 7 \\ - 1 \\ \hline \end{array}$$
☐

㊹
$$\begin{array}{r} 8 \\ - 1 \\ \hline \end{array}$$
☐

Complete. Write + or − in ◯ .

㊺ ____ ◯ ____ = ____

㊻ ____ ◯ ____ = ____

㊼ ____ ◯ ____ = ____

㊽ ____ ◯ ____ = ____

Complete each number sentence. Write + or − in ◯ .

㊾ There are 8 ✏ . Buy 1 ✏ more . How many ✏ are there in all?

____ ◯ ____ = ____   ____ ✏ in all.

㊿ There are 7 🍊 . 1 🍊 is eaten. How many 🍊 are left?

____ ◯ ____ = ____   ____ 🍊 left.

51 There are 6 🦜 . 1 🦜 flies away. How many 🦜 are left?

____ ◯ ____ = ____   ____ 🦜 left.

Just for Fun

Write the missing numbers.

Addition Facts to 6

4 and 2; 6 in all

4 + 2 = 6

$$\begin{array}{r} 4 \\ +\ 2 \\ \hline 6 \end{array}$$

HINTS:

* Vertical addition:

$$\begin{array}{r} 3 \\ +\ 1 \\ \hline 4 \end{array}$$ ← align on the right-hand side

* Matching addition sentence:

3 + 1 = 4

Complete each addition sentence.

① +

____ 2 ____ + ____ 3 ____ = ____ 5 ____

② +

____ + ____ = ____

③ +   ____ + ____ = ____

④ +   ____ + ____ = ____

⑤ +   ____ + ____ = ____

⑥   ____ + ____ = ____

⑦ +   ____ + ____ = ____

⑧ +   ____ + ____ = ____

Add.

⑨ 3 + 3 = ☐   ⑩ 3 + 2 = ☐

⑪ 1 + 4 = ☐   ⑫ 1 + 2 = ☐

⑬ 4 + 2 = ☐   ⑭ 2 + 2 = ☐

⑮ 2 + 3 = ☐   ⑯ 5 + 1 = ☐

⑰ 2 + 4 = ☐   ⑱ 1 + 1 = ☐

⑲ 3 + 1 = ☐   ⑳ 4 + 1 = ☐

㉑ 1 + 5 = ☐   ㉒ 1 + 3 = ☐

㉓ 3
  + 3
  ☐

㉔ 2
  + 4
  ☐

㉕ 2
  + 2
  ☐

㉖ 2
  + 1
  ☐

㉗ 3
  + 2
  ☐

㉘ 1
  + 5
  ☐

㉙ 2
  + 3
  ☐

㉚ 1
  + 4
  ☐

㉛ 1
  + 2
  ☐

㉜ 4
  + 2
  ☐

㉝ 5
  + 1
  ☐

㉞ 1
  + 3
  ☐

Match.

③⑤

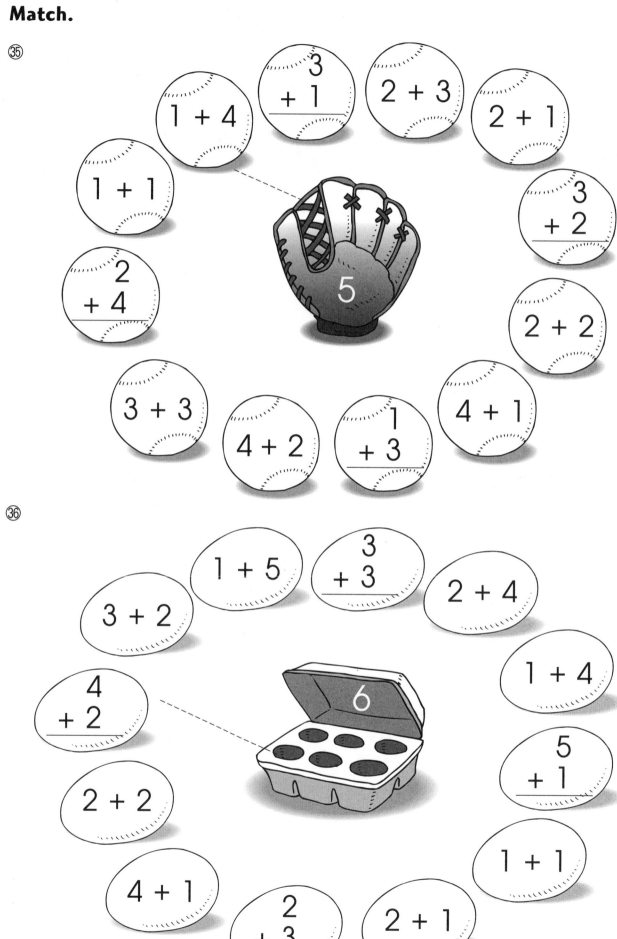

③⑥

Colour the two sets of beads that make each bracelet. Write addition sentences to match.

③⑦

_____ + _____ = _____

③⑧

_____ + _____ = _____

Complete each addition sentence.

③⑨ There are 3 and 2 . How many   are there?

_____ + _____ = _____   There are _____ .

④⓪ There are 4 and 2 . How many   are there?

_____ + _____ = _____   There are _____ .

④① There are 3 and 3 . How many are there?

_____ + _____ = _____   There are _____ .

Match.

| 2 + 3 | 1 + 3 | 2 + 4 | 2 + 1 |

●   ●   ●   ●

●   ●   ●   ●

| 2 + 2 | 4 + 1 | 1 + 2 | 3 + 3 |

Subtraction Facts to 6

E X A M P L E

$$\begin{array}{r} 6 \\ -\ 2 \\ \hline 4 \end{array}$$

Take away 2; 4 are left.
6 – 2 = 4

HINTS:

- Vertical subtraction:

  $$\begin{array}{r} 3 \\ -\ 2 \\ \hline 1 \end{array}$$ ← align on the right-hand side

- Matching subtraction sentence:

  3 – 2 = 1

Complete each subtraction sentence.

①

 _5_ – _3_ = _2_

② ✏✏ ✗ ✗

_____ – _____ = _____

③ 🏐🏐🏐🏐 ✗ ✗

_____ – _____ = _____

④ 🍬🍬🍬 ✗ ✗

_____ – _____ = _____

⑤ 🍊🍊 ✗ ✗ ✗

_____ – _____ = _____

⑥ 🧁 ✗ ✗ ✗ ✗

_____ – _____ = _____

⑦ 🔘 ✗ ✗

_____ – _____ = _____

⑧ 🍎🍎🍎 ✗ ✗ ✗

_____ – _____ = _____

56   COMPLETE MATHSMART (GRADE 1)

Subtract.

⑨ 4 − 2 = ☐

⑩ 6 − 1 = ☐

⑪ 6 − 5 = ☐

⑫ 5 − 4 = ☐

⑬ 5 − 3 = ☐

⑭ 4 − 3 = ☐

⑮ 6 − 2 = ☐

⑯ 5 − 2 = ☐

⑰ 3 − 2 = ☐

⑱ 6 − 4 = ☐

⑲ 6 − 3 = ☐

⑳ 4 − 1 = ☐

㉑ 5 − 1 = ☐

㉒ 3 − 1 = ☐

㉓
$$\begin{array}{r} 5 \\ -\ 4 \\ \hline \end{array}$$
☐

㉔
$$\begin{array}{r} 4 \\ -\ 2 \\ \hline \end{array}$$
☐

㉕
$$\begin{array}{r} 6 \\ -\ 2 \\ \hline \end{array}$$
☐

㉖
$$\begin{array}{r} 3 \\ -\ 1 \\ \hline \end{array}$$
☐

㉗
$$\begin{array}{r} 6 \\ -\ 4 \\ \hline \end{array}$$
☐

㉘
$$\begin{array}{r} 5 \\ -\ 3 \\ \hline \end{array}$$
☐

㉙
$$\begin{array}{r} 4 \\ -\ 3 \\ \hline \end{array}$$
☐

㉚
$$\begin{array}{r} 5 \\ -\ 2 \\ \hline \end{array}$$
☐

㉛
$$\begin{array}{r} 3 \\ -\ 2 \\ \hline \end{array}$$
☐

㉜
$$\begin{array}{r} 6 \\ -\ 3 \\ \hline \end{array}$$
☐

㉝
$$\begin{array}{r} 5 \\ -\ 1 \\ \hline \end{array}$$
☐

㉞
$$\begin{array}{r} 6 \\ -\ 5 \\ \hline \end{array}$$
☐

Match.

㉟

㊱

Which bunches are the fruit on the plates cut from? Colour the right bunches and complete the subtraction sentences.

③⑦

$$\underline{\qquad} - 2 = \underline{\qquad}$$

③⑧

$$\underline{\qquad} - 3 = \underline{\qquad}$$

Complete each subtraction sentence.

③⑨

How many are left?

$$\underline{\qquad} - \underline{\qquad} = \underline{\qquad}$$

④⓪

How many are left?

$$\underline{\qquad} - \underline{\qquad} = \underline{\qquad}$$

④①

How many are left?

$$\underline{\qquad} - \underline{\qquad} = \underline{\qquad}$$

④②

How many are left?

$$\underline{\qquad} - \underline{\qquad} = \underline{\qquad}$$

④③

How many are left?

$$\underline{\qquad} - \underline{\qquad} = \underline{\qquad}$$

④④

How many are left?

$$\underline{\qquad} - \underline{\qquad} = \underline{\qquad}$$

Match.

| 1 | 2 | 3 | 4 |

4 - 2   6 - 2   5 - 4   4 - 1

Addition and Subtraction of 0

E X A M P L E S

None goes.   5 − 0 = 5

None comes.   5 + 0 = 5

HINTS:

- " 0 " means NONE.
- Any number plus 0 equals itself.
- Any number minus 0 equals itself.

How many are there?

① _____

② _____

③ _____

④ _____

⑤ _____

Complete each number sentence.

⑥

3 + 1 = _____

⑦

3 + 0 = _____

⑧

6 − 1 = _____

⑨

6 − 0 = _____

Add or subtract.

⑩ 6 + 0 = 6

⑪ 6 − 0 = ☐

⑫ 5 + 0 = ☐

⑬ 5 − 0 = ☐

⑭ 4 + 0 = ☐

⑮ 4 − 0 = ☐

⑯ 3 + 0 = ☐

⑰ 3 − 0 = ☐

⑱ 2 + 0 = ☐

⑲ 2 − 0 = ☐

⑳ 1 + 0 = ☐

㉑ 1 − 0 = ☐

㉒ 0 + 0 = ☐

㉓ 0 − 0 = ☐

㉔
```
   5
+  0
―――
 ☐
```

㉕
```
   0
+  4
―――
 ☐
```

㉖
```
   3
−  0
―――
 ☐
```

㉗
```
   0
+  1
―――
 ☐
```

㉘
```
   0
+  6
―――
 ☐
```

㉙
```
   3
+  0
―――
 ☐
```

㉚
```
   0
+  5
―――
 ☐
```

㉛
```
   6
−  0
―――
 ☐
```

㉜
```
   4
−  0
―――
 ☐
```

㉝
```
   0
+  2
―――
 ☐
```

㉞
```
   4
+  0
―――
 ☐
```

㉟
```
   2
−  0
―――
 ☐
```

Match.

Add or subtract 0.

㊲ Add 0		㊳ Subtract 0		㊴ Add 0		㊵ Subtract 0	
4	*4*	5		1		6	
2		3		3		2	
6		1		5		4	

Complete.

㊶ 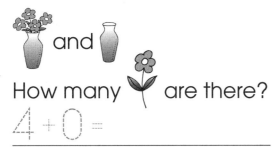 and

How many 🌸 are there?

4 + 0 =

_____ 🌸 in all.

㊷ and

How many 🐟 are there?

_____

_____ 🐟 in all.

㊸ 0 fish taken away.

How many 🐟 are left?

_____

_____ 🐟 left.

㊹ 0 🌀 rolls off.

How many 🌀 are left?

_____

_____ 🌀 left.

Just for Fun

Count back to help Little Bee find the path to the hive.

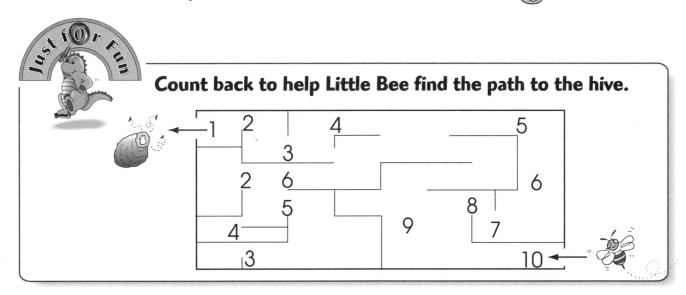

5 Addition and Subtraction Facts to 6

1. The sum of 3 and 2 is 5.

2. The difference between 5 and 2 is 3.

HINTS:

- Addition
  $3 + 2 = 5$ ←——— sum

- Subtraction
  $5 - 2 = 3$ ←——— difference

**Complete each number sentence. Put + or –
in .**

① $4 \; \bigcirc \; 2 \; = \; 6$

② ___ $\bigcirc$ ___ = ___

③ ___ $\bigcirc$ ___ = ___

④ ___ $\bigcirc$ ___ = ___

⑤ ___ $\bigcirc$ ___ = ___

⑥ ___ $\bigcirc$ ___ = ___

Add or subtract.

⑦ $4 - 3 =$ ☐   ⑧ $2 + 2 =$ ☐

⑨ $3 + 1 =$ ☐   ⑩ $5 - 2 =$ ☐

⑪ $4 + 2 =$ ☐   ⑫ $6 - 3 =$ ☐

⑬ $3 + 3 =$ ☐   ⑭ $3 + 0 =$ ☐

⑮ $1 - 1 =$ ☐   ⑯ $4 - 2 =$ ☐

⑰ $5 - 3 =$ ☐   ⑱ $2 + 1 =$ ☐

⑲ $6 - 2 =$ ☐   ⑳ $2 + 3 =$ ☐

㉑
$$\begin{array}{r} 5 \\ + \ 0 \\ \hline \end{array}$$
☐

㉒
$$\begin{array}{r} 6 \\ - \ 5 \\ \hline \end{array}$$
☐

㉓
$$\begin{array}{r} 4 \\ - \ 0 \\ \hline \end{array}$$
☐

㉔
$$\begin{array}{r} 2 \\ - \ 1 \\ \hline \end{array}$$
☐

㉕
$$\begin{array}{r} 4 \\ + \ 1 \\ \hline \end{array}$$
☐

㉖
$$\begin{array}{r} 5 \\ - \ 4 \\ \hline \end{array}$$
☐

㉗
$$\begin{array}{r} 3 \\ - \ 2 \\ \hline \end{array}$$
☐

㉘
$$\begin{array}{r} 6 \\ + \ 0 \\ \hline \end{array}$$
☐

㉙
$$\begin{array}{r} 2 \\ - \ 0 \\ \hline \end{array}$$
☐

㉚
$$\begin{array}{r} 6 \\ - \ 4 \\ \hline \end{array}$$
☐

㉛
$$\begin{array}{r} 1 \\ + \ 1 \\ \hline \end{array}$$
☐

㉜
$$\begin{array}{r} 4 \\ - \ 0 \\ \hline \end{array}$$
☐

Find the sums or differences. Help the snake get back to the hole.

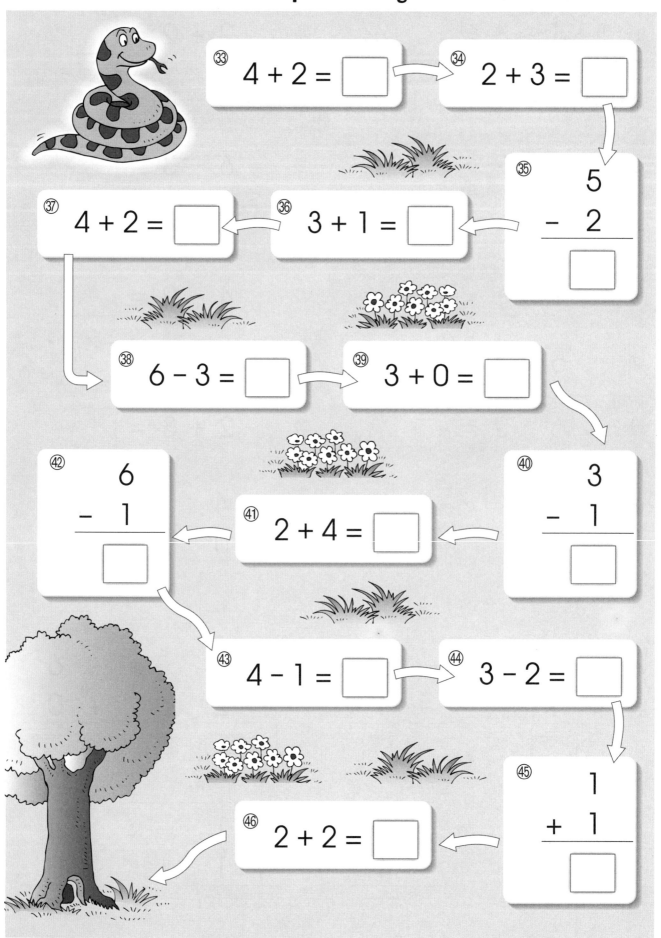

33 4 + 2 = ☐

34 2 + 3 = ☐

35
$$\begin{array}{r} 5 \\ -\ 2 \\ \hline \square \end{array}$$

36 3 + 1 = ☐

37 4 + 2 = ☐

38 6 − 3 = ☐

39 3 + 0 = ☐

40
$$\begin{array}{r} 3 \\ -\ 1 \\ \hline \square \end{array}$$

41 2 + 4 = ☐

42
$$\begin{array}{r} 6 \\ -\ 1 \\ \hline \square \end{array}$$

43 4 − 1 = ☐

44 3 − 2 = ☐

45
$$\begin{array}{r} 1 \\ +\ 1 \\ \hline \square \end{array}$$

46 2 + 2 = ☐

Complete.

㊼ There are 4 🍎 ; 2 🍎 are eaten. How many 🍎 are left?

4 – 2 =

_____ 🍎 left.

㊽ There are 4 🍎 and 2 🍎. How many 🍎 🍎 are there in all?

_____

_____ 🍎 🍎 in all.

㊾ There are 3 ✏ and 3 ✏. How many ✏ ✏ are there in all?

_____

_____ ✏ ✏ in all.

㊿ There are 6 🥚; 4 🥚 are broken. How many 🥚 are left?

_____

_____ 🥚 left.

�51 There are 5 🎈 ; 2 🎈 burst. How many 🎈 are left?

_____

_____ 🎈 left.

�52 Sue has 5 🍐; 1 🍐 is eaten. How many 🍐 are left?

_____

_____ 🍐 left.

Add or Subtract. Match the answers with the words.

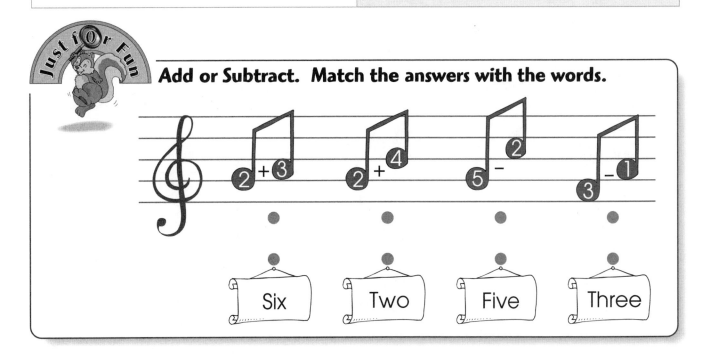

2 + 3   2 + 4   5 – 2   3 – 1

Six   Two   Five   Three

Addition Facts to 10

1. 6 and 4 ; 10 in all. → $6 + 4 = 10$

2. 2 and 7 ; 9 in all. → $2 + 7 = 9$

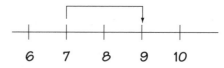

HINTS:

- Adding 2 numbers:

  Count on from the bigger number

  $7 + 2 = ?$ ← start from 7 and count 2 numbers more

  $7 \rightarrow 8 \rightarrow 9$ or

  Use a number line to find the sum.

  | 6 | 7 | 8 | 9 | 10 |

  $7 + 2 = 9$

Complete each addition sentence.

①

  _6_ + _3_ = _____

②

  _____ + _____ = _____

③

  _____ + _____ = _____

④

  _____ + _____ = _____

⑤

  _____ + _____ = _____

⑥

  _____ + _____ = _____

⑦

  _____ + _____ = _____

Add.

⑧ 5 + 4 = ☐   ⑨ 7 + 3 = ☐

⑩ 9 + 1 = ☐   ⑪ 6 + 3 = ☐

⑫ 7 + 2 = ☐   ⑬ 8 + 2 = ☐

⑭ 8 + 1 = ☐   ⑮ 6 + 4 = ☐

⑯ 6 + 2 = ☐   ⑰ 5 + 3 = ☐

⑱ 5 + 2 = ☐   ⑲ 3 + 4 = ☐

⑳ 10 + 0 = ☐   ㉑ 4 + 4 = ☐

㉒
```
   3
 + 6
 ────
 ☐
```

㉓
```
   2
 + 8
 ────
 ☐
```

㉔
```
   3
 + 5
 ────
 ☐
```

㉕
```
   2
 + 7
 ────
 ☐
```

㉖
```
   8
 + 0
 ────
 ☐
```

㉗
```
   6
 + 2
 ────
 ☐
```

㉘
```
   9
 + 0
 ────
 ☐
```

㉙
```
   7
 + 3
 ────
 ☐
```

㉚
```
   3
 + 4
 ────
 ☐
```

㉛
```
   4
 + 5
 ────
 ☐
```

㉜
```
   7
 + 0
 ────
 ☐
```

㉝
```
   4
 + 3
 ────
 ☐
```

Complete the addition sentences for each number family. Draw the correct number of items.

 ㉞ 9

$9 = \underline{\quad 5 \quad} + \underline{\quad 4 \quad}$

 ㉟ 9

$9 = \underline{\qquad} + \underline{\qquad}$

㊱ 9

$9 = \underline{\qquad} + \underline{\qquad}$

㊲ 9

$9 = \underline{\qquad} + \underline{\qquad}$

㊳ 9

$9 = \underline{\qquad} + \underline{\qquad}$

㊴ 8

$8 = \underline{\qquad} + \underline{\qquad}$

㊵ 8

$8 = \underline{\qquad} + \underline{\qquad}$

㊶ 8

$8 = \underline{\qquad} + \underline{\qquad}$

㊷ 8

$8 = \underline{\qquad} + \underline{\qquad}$

㊸ 8

$8 = \underline{\qquad} + \underline{\qquad}$

㊹ 7

$7 = \underline{\qquad} + \underline{\qquad}$

㊺ 7

$7 = \underline{\qquad} + \underline{\qquad}$

㊻ 7

$7 = \underline{\qquad} + \underline{\qquad}$

㊼ 7

$7 = \underline{\qquad} + \underline{\qquad}$

Add.

㊽

㊾

Complete.

㊿ Sue has . Sam has . How many are there in all?

_____ + _____ = _____   _____ in all.

�51 Jack has . Jane has . How many are there in all?

_____ + _____ = _____   _____ in all.

�52 Bob has . Ben has . How many are there in all?

_____ + _____ = _____   _____ in all.

Fill in the missing numbers.

Subtraction Facts to 10

EXAMPLES

1. 8 ; 2 were taken away ; 6 were left.

| $8 - 2 = 6$ |

2. 9 ; 4 flew away ; 5 were left.

| $9 - 4 = 5$ |

Complete each subtraction sentence.

HINTS:

- Subtracting 2 numbers:

  Count back from the bigger number.

  $9 - 3 = ?$ → start from 9 and count 3 numbers back

  $9 \rightarrow 8 \rightarrow 7 \rightarrow 6$ or

  Use a number line to find the difference.

  $9 - 3 = 6$

①

     9 $-$ 3 $=$ _____

②

_____ $-$ _____ $=$ _____

③

_____ $-$ _____ $=$ _____

④

_____ $-$ _____ $=$ _____

⑤

_____ $-$ _____ $=$ _____

⑥

_____ $-$ _____ $=$ _____

⑦

_____ $-$ _____ $=$ _____

72   COMPLETE MATHSMART (GRADE 1)

Subtract.

⑧ 9 – 3 = ☐   ⑨ 8 – 2 = ☐

⑩ 10 – 4 = ☐   ⑪ 7 – 5 = ☐

⑫ 8 – 3 = ☐   ⑬ 10 – 5 = ☐

⑭ 9 – 4 = ☐   ⑮ 8 – 7 = ☐

⑯ 7 – 6 = ☐   ⑰ 10 – 8 = ☐

⑱ 9 – 7 = ☐   ⑲ 7 – 3 = ☐

⑳ 10 – 6 = ☐   ㉑ 9 – 6 = ☐

㉒
$$\begin{array}{r} 7 \\ -\ 4 \\ \hline \square \end{array}$$
㉓
$$\begin{array}{r} 10 \\ -\ 9 \\ \hline \square \end{array}$$
㉔
$$\begin{array}{r} 8 \\ -\ 6 \\ \hline \square \end{array}$$
㉕
$$\begin{array}{r} 9 \\ -\ 5 \\ \hline \square \end{array}$$

㉖
$$\begin{array}{r} 9 \\ -\ 8 \\ \hline \square \end{array}$$
㉗
$$\begin{array}{r} 8 \\ -\ 6 \\ \hline \square \end{array}$$
㉘
$$\begin{array}{r} 10 \\ -\ 7 \\ \hline \square \end{array}$$
㉙
$$\begin{array}{r} 7 \\ -\ 2 \\ \hline \square \end{array}$$

㉚
$$\begin{array}{r} 10 \\ -\ 2 \\ \hline \square \end{array}$$
㉛
$$\begin{array}{r} 8 \\ -\ 4 \\ \hline \square \end{array}$$
㉜
$$\begin{array}{r} 10 \\ -\ 0 \\ \hline \square \end{array}$$
㉝
$$\begin{array}{r} 9 \\ -\ 1 \\ \hline \square \end{array}$$

Match and complete. Write the letters in ㊺ to solve the riddle.

㉞ $10 - 5 =$ 5

㉟ $8 - 4 =$ ☐

㊱ $10 - 2 =$ ☐

㊲ $10 - 0 =$ ☐

㊳ $7 - 6 =$ ☐

㊴ $8 - 8 =$ ☐

㊵ $9 - 6 =$ ☐

㊶ $10 - 1 =$ ☐

㊷ $7 - 5 =$ ☐

㊸ $6 - 0 =$ ☐

㊹ $9 - 2 =$ ☐

$10 - 0 =$ ☐ (H)

$8 - 0 =$ ☐ (U)

$9 - 4 =$ 5 (I)

$7 - 3 =$ ☐ (A)

$8 - 5 =$ ☐ (S)

$9 - 0 =$ ☐ (R)

$8 - 7 =$ ☐ (L)

$7 - 7 =$ ☐ (B)

$8 - 2 =$ ☐ (T)

$10 - 3 =$ ☐ (M)

$10 - 8 =$ ☐ (O)

Riddle: Which is the westernmost province in Canada?

㊺

0	9	5	6	5	3	10	2	1	8	7	0	5	4
							C						

Subtract.

㊻

㊼

Complete.

㊽ Sue has . fly away. How many are left?

_____ – _____ = _____   _____ left.

㊾ Jack has . are eaten. How many are left?

_____ – _____ = _____   _____ left.

㊿ Mom has . are broken. How many

are left?

_____ – _____ = _____   _____ left.

Use – and = to make a subtraction sentence in each row. Circle each hidden subtraction sentence.

8	10 – 2 = 8	6
9	7 6 3	3
6	5 1 7	1
9	5 4 10	6

Addition and Subtraction Facts to 10

There are and   and   .

How many are there in all?

1 + 2 + 4 = 7

7 in all.

$$\begin{array}{r} 1 \\ +\quad 2 \\ \hline 3 \end{array} \rightarrow \begin{array}{r} 3 \\ +\quad 4 \\ \hline 7 \end{array} \qquad \begin{array}{r} 1 \\ 2 \\ +\quad 4 \\ \hline 7 \end{array}$$

HINTS:

Adding 3 numbers:

Add the first 2 numbers. Write down the sum or bear it in mind. Then add the sum to the last number.

Complete each number sentence.

①

    5 + 4 _____ = _____

②

    _____ = _____

③

    _____ = _____

④   ///

    _____ = _____

⑤

    _____ = _____

⑥

    _____ = _____

Add or subtract.

⑦ 2 + 2 + 3 = ☐   ⑧ 8 – 6 = ☐

⑨ 10 – 4 = ☐   ⑩ 6 + 4 = ☐

⑪ 7 + 2 = ☐   ⑫ 9 – 6 = ☐

⑬ 7 – 5 = ☐   ⑭ 1 + 0 + 6 = ☐

⑮ 8 + 2 = ☐   ⑯ 7 – 6 = ☐

⑰ 1 + 1 + 5 = ☐   ⑱ 9 – 2 = ☐

⑲ 6 + 3 = ☐   ⑳ 5 + 5 = ☐

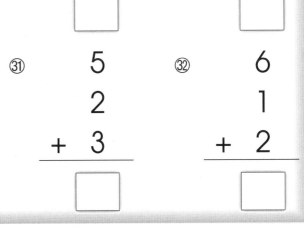

㉑
```
  8
+ 0
───
  ☐
```
㉒
```
  4
+ 5
───
  ☐
```
㉓
```
  2
+ 7
───
  ☐
```
㉔
```
  4
+ 4
───
  ☐
```

㉕
```
  9
– 8
───
  ☐
```
㉖
```
 10
– 7
───
  ☐
```
㉗
```
  7
– 5
───
  ☐
```
㉘
```
  8
– 3
───
  ☐
```

㉙
```
  2
  0
+ 5
───
  ☐
```
㉚
```
  3
  1
+ 4
───
  ☐
```
㉛
```
  5
  2
+ 3
───
  ☐
```
㉜
```
  6
  1
+ 2
───
  ☐
```

Add or subtract. Help the cat find the path to the milk.

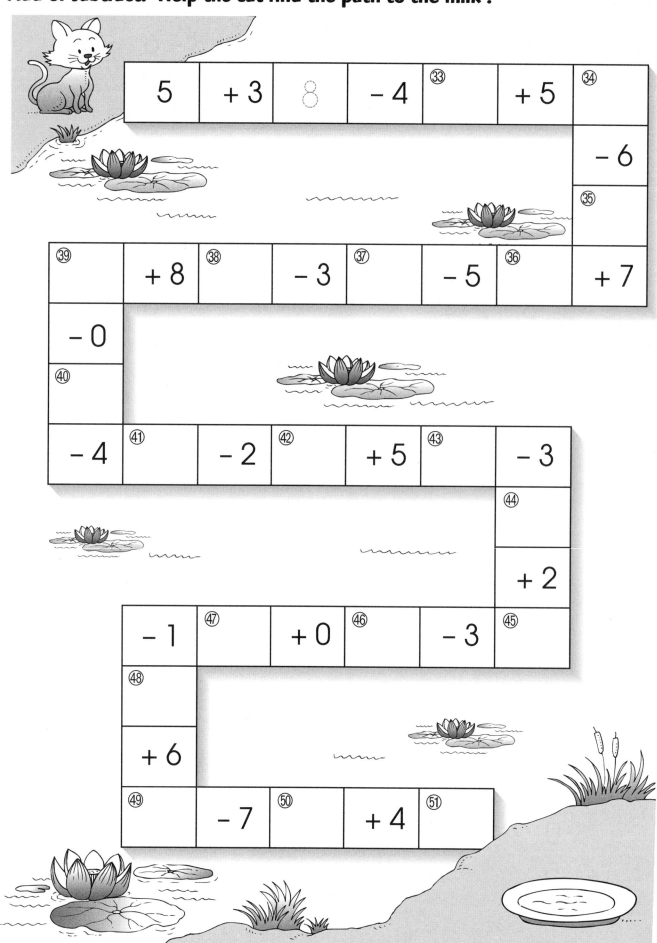

| 5 | + 3 | 8 | − 4 | ㉝ | + 5 | ㉞ |

− 6

㉟ + 7

| ㊴ | + 8 | ㊳ | − 3 | ㊲ | − 5 | ㊱ |

− 0

㊵

| − 4 | ㊶ | − 2 | ㊷ | + 5 | ㊸ | − 3 |

㊹

+ 2

| − 1 | ㊼ | + 0 | ㊻ | − 3 | ㊺ |

㊽

+ 6

| ㊾ | − 7 | ㊿ | + 4 | 51 |

Complete.

⑤② 8 🐦 were in a tree. 2 flew away. How many 🐦 were left in the tree? _____ 🐦 left.	8 — 2
⑤③ 6 🐢 were on a rock. 4 more came. How many 🐢 were on the rock? _____ 🐢 were on the rock.	
⑤④ Sam has 5 🐚. Sue has 4 🐚. How many 🐚 do they have altogether? _____ 🐚 altogether.	
⑤⑤ 9 🐒 were in a tree. 6 jumped down. How many 🐒 were left in the tree? _____ 🐒 left.	
⑤⑥ Sue has 2 🍭. Sam has 4 🍭. Ann has 1 🍭. How many 🍭 do they have altogether? _____ 🍭 altogether.	

Pick out any two balls each time.

The smallest sum is _____.

The largest difference is _____.

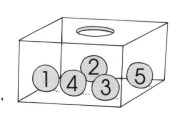

Midway | Review

Complete each number sentence.

①   _____ = ____

②   _____ = ____

③   _____ = ____

Find the sums or differences.

④ 10 − 5 = ☐		⑤ 4 + 2 = ☐	
⑥ 9 − 7 = ☐		⑦ 8 − 6 = ☐	
⑧ 2 + 5 = ☐		⑨ 6 − 5 = ☐	
⑩ 3 + 3 = ☐		⑪ 7 + 0 = ☐	
⑫ 6 + 0 + 3 = ☐		⑬ 4 + 1 + 2 = ☐	

⑭
$$\begin{array}{r} 0 \\ +\ 9 \\ \hline \end{array}$$
☐

⑮
$$\begin{array}{r} 5 \\ -\ 4 \\ \hline \end{array}$$
☐

⑯
$$\begin{array}{r} 10 \\ -\ 7 \\ \hline \end{array}$$
☐

⑰
$$\begin{array}{r} 3 \\ +\ 5 \\ \hline \end{array}$$
☐

⑱
$$\begin{array}{r} 6 \\ -\ 4 \\ \hline \end{array}$$
☐

⑲
$$\begin{array}{r} 3 \\ +\ 4 \\ \hline \end{array}$$
☐

⑳
$$\begin{array}{r} 8 \\ -\ 4 \\ \hline \end{array}$$
☐

㉑
$$\begin{array}{r} 1 \\ +\ 7 \\ \hline \end{array}$$
☐

In each group, colour the pieces that match the number.

㉒ 8   5 + 3   10 − 2   3 + 6   9 − 1

㉓ 6   4 + 1   9 − 3   8 − 2   3 + 3

㉔ 9   1 + 8   10 − 2   5 + 4   9 − 0

㉕ 5   10 − 5   3 + 2   8 − 2   4 + 1

㉖ 7   4 + 3   9 − 2   10 − 3   2 + 6

Complete the tables. Write + or − in ◯ .

㉗

+ 3	
2	5
7	
5	

㉘

− 4	
8	
4	
6	

㉙

◯	2
9	7
5	3
6	4

㉚

◯	4
2	6
6	10
5	9

Write the numbers.

③① 10 – ☐

③③ 9 – ☐

③⑤ 8 – ☐

③⑦ 7 – ☐

5

③② 3 + ☐

③④ 2 + ☐

③⑥ 1 + ☐

③⑧ 0 + ☐

Put + or – in each box.

③⑨
```
   10
☐  2
────
   8
```

④⓪
```
   2
☐  7
────
   9
```

④①
```
   5
☐  4
────
   9
```

④②
```
   8
☐  6
────
   2
```

④③
```
   7
☐  5
────
   2
```

④④
```
   3
☐  4
────
   7
```

④⑤
```
   9
☐  3
────
   6
```

④⑥
```
   1
☐  5
────
   6
```

④⑦
```
   8
☐  4
────
   4
```

④⑧
```
   9
☐  1
────
   8
```

④⑨
```
   4
☐  2
────
   6
```

⑤⓪
```
   3
☐  6
────
   9
```

Fill in the numbers.

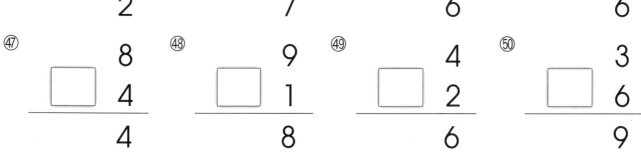

⑤① 6 + ☐ = 7

⑤② 1 + ☐ = 4

⑤③ 6 – ☐ = 2

⑤④ 7 – ☐ = 3

⑤⑤ 4 + ☐ = 8

⑤⑥ 2 + ☐ = 5

Complete.

57 10 🐦 are in the sky. 2 🐦 land on the grass. How many 🐦 are left in the sky? _____ 🐦 left.	
58 6 🐸 are in a pond. 3 🐸 jump away. How many 🐸 are left in the pond? _____ 🐸 left.	
59 5 🪰 are in the sky. 4 🪰 are on the water. How many 🪰 are there in all? _____ 🪰 in all.	
60 There are 2 🌹 and 6 🌹 . How many 🌹 🌹 are there in all? _____ 🌹 🌹 in all.	
61 4 🐒 are in the tree. 3 🐒 are on the grass. How many 🐒 are there in all? _____ 🐒 in all.	
62 8 🍌 are in the tree. The 🐒 eats 4 🍌. How many 🍌 are left in the tree? _____ 🍌 left.	

Addition Facts to 15

$8 + 7 = 15$

HINTS:

- Counting on helps you find the sum faster.
- Different addition sentences may give the same SUM.

Draw the lines. Complete the addition sentences.

①

$6 + \underline{9} = 15$

②

$6 + \underline{} = 13$

③

$\underline{} + 4 = 12$

④

$10 + \underline{} = \underline{}$

⑤

$\underline{} + 1 = \underline{}$

⑥

$\underline{} + 9 = \underline{}$

Add.

⑦	12 + 3 = ☐		⑧	11 + 2 = ☐
⑨	10 + 4 = ☐		⑩	9 + 6 = ☐
⑪	8 + 6 = ☐		⑫	7 + 5 = ☐
⑬	9 + 3 = ☐		⑭	6 + 7 = ☐
⑮	14 + 0 = ☐		⑯	2 + 9 = ☐
⑰	3 + 8 = ☐		⑱	5 + 6 = ☐
⑲	7 + 7 = ☐		⑳	13 + 2 = ☐

㉑
$$\begin{array}{r} 4 \\ +\ 9 \\ \hline \end{array}$$
☐

㉒
$$\begin{array}{r} 11 \\ +\ 4 \\ \hline \end{array}$$
☐

㉓
$$\begin{array}{r} 6 \\ +\ 6 \\ \hline \end{array}$$
☐

㉔
$$\begin{array}{r} 7 \\ +\ 4 \\ \hline \end{array}$$
☐

㉕
$$\begin{array}{r} 8 \\ +\ 4 \\ \hline \end{array}$$
☐

㉖
$$\begin{array}{r} 9 \\ +\ 5 \\ \hline \end{array}$$
☐

㉗
$$\begin{array}{r} 5 \\ +\ 8 \\ \hline \end{array}$$
☐

㉘
$$\begin{array}{r} 11 \\ +\ 3 \\ \hline \end{array}$$
☐

㉙
$$\begin{array}{r} 14 \\ +\ 1 \\ \hline \end{array}$$
☐

㉚
$$\begin{array}{r} 7 \\ +\ 8 \\ \hline \end{array}$$
☐

㉛
$$\begin{array}{r} 9 \\ +\ 6 \\ \hline \end{array}$$
☐

㉜
$$\begin{array}{r} 12 \\ +\ 2 \\ \hline \end{array}$$
☐

Fill in the missing numbers.

㉝ 3 + ☐

㉟ 4 + ☐

㊲ 5 + ☐

㊴ 6 + ☐

㊶ 7 + ☐

14

㉞ 8 + ☐

㊱ 9 + ☐

㊳ 10 + ☐

㊵ 11 + ☐

㊷ 12 + ☐

Complete. Colour the balloon with the largest sum in each group.

㊸

A
5
+ 6
☐

B
8
+ 4
☐

C
7
+ 6
☐

D
9
+ 6
☐

㊹

A
11
+ 2
☐

B
10
+ 4
☐

C
2
+ 9
☐

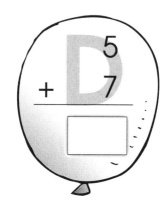
D
5
+ 7
☐

㊺ 3 + 8 A = _____

6 + 6 B = _____

11 + 3 C = _____

㊻ 12 + 3 A = _____

6 + 8 B = _____

9 + 3 C = _____

Complete.

㊼ There are 8 red and 6 green .

How many are there in all?

_____ in all.

$$\begin{array}{r} 8 \\ + \ 6 \\ \hline \end{array}$$

㊽ 10 are on the plate.
3 are in the bag.

How many are there in all?

_____ in all.

㊾ 12 are in the basket.
0 are on the table.

How many are there in all?

_____ in all.

㊿ 4 are in Sam's left hand.
7 are in his right hand.

How many does Sam have in all?

_____ in all.

Complete.

$$9 + 6 = 10 + \boxed{}$$

$$2 + 5 = 8 - \boxed{}$$

10 Subtraction Facts to 15

$15 - 4 = 11$

HINTS:

- Counting back helps you find the difference faster.

- Different subtraction sentences may give the same DIFFERENCE.

Follow the example to complete each subtraction sentence.

①

14 $- 6 =$ _____

②

_____ $- 7 =$ _____

③

_____ $- 8 =$ _____

④

_____ $- 10 =$ _____

⑤

_____ $- 9 =$ _____

⑥

_____ $- 11 =$ _____

Subtract.

⑦ 13 − 4 = ☐ ⑧ 12 − 6 = ☐

⑨ 15 − 7 = ☐ ⑩ 14 − 9 = ☐

⑪ 11 − 6 = ☐ ⑫ 13 − 8 = ☐

⑬ 12 − 8 = ☐ ⑭ 15 − 9 = ☐

⑮ 14 − 4 = ☐ ⑯ 13 − 0 = ☐

⑰ 13 − 2 = ☐ ⑱ 11 − 3 = ☐

⑲ 15 − 13 = ☐ ⑳ 12 − 3 = ☐

㉑
$$\begin{array}{r} 11 \\ -\ 7 \\ \hline \end{array}$$
☐

㉒
$$\begin{array}{r} 13 \\ -\ 1 \\ \hline \end{array}$$
☐

㉓
$$\begin{array}{r} 15 \\ -\ 5 \\ \hline \end{array}$$
☐

㉔
$$\begin{array}{r} 12 \\ -\ 12 \\ \hline \end{array}$$
☐

㉕
$$\begin{array}{r} 14 \\ -\ 10 \\ \hline \end{array}$$
☐

㉖
$$\begin{array}{r} 15 \\ -\ 9 \\ \hline \end{array}$$
☐

㉗
$$\begin{array}{r} 12 \\ -\ 4 \\ \hline \end{array}$$
☐

㉘
$$\begin{array}{r} 11 \\ -\ 4 \\ \hline \end{array}$$
☐

㉙
$$\begin{array}{r} 13 \\ -\ 9 \\ \hline \end{array}$$
☐

㉚
$$\begin{array}{r} 14 \\ -\ 12 \\ \hline \end{array}$$
☐

㉛
$$\begin{array}{r} 11 \\ -\ 5 \\ \hline \end{array}$$
☐

㉜
$$\begin{array}{r} 12 \\ -\ 7 \\ \hline \end{array}$$
☐

Subtract. Help Baby Bear find Mother Bear.

33 14 – 7 =

34 13 – 5 =

37 11 – 2 =

35
1 2
– 5

38
1 3
– 1 1

36 15 – 6 =

39 14 – 8 =

40 12 – 2 =

41 13 – 3 =

42
1 1
– 8

43 14 – 5 =

Complete.

㊹ There are 14 🍎. 8 🍎 are eaten.
How many 🍎 are left?

    14
   − 8
   ‾‾‾‾‾

_____ 🍎 left.

㊺ Sue has 12 🐚. Sam has 7 🐚.
How many more 🐚 does Sue have than Sam?

_____ more 🐚.

㊻ There are 13 🍪 on the plate and 5 🍪 in the bag.
How many more 🍪 are there on the plate?

_____ more 🍪.

㊼ There are 15 🎈. 6 🎈 burst. How many 🎈 are left?

_____ 🎈 left.

Count on to find the path for the monkey.
Colour the path.

12	18	16	17	15
14	16	15	18	17
15	13	14	19	20
11	12	17	18	16
17	13	12	11	12

EXAMPLES

There are 12 and 3 .

1. How many are there in all?

    12 + 3 = 15   15 🍐🍐 in all.

2. How many more 🍐 are there than 🍐 ?

    12 − 3 = 9   9 more 🍐 .

HINTS:

- Vertical addition:

        1 2
    +   3   ← align on the right-hand side
    ―――――
        1 5

- Vertical subtraction:

        1 2
    −   3   ← align on the right-hand side
    ―――――
          9

Add or cross out the correct number of items. Complete each number sentence.

①

    15 − 6 = _____

②

    9 + __5__ = 14

③

    7 + ____ = 15

④

    ____ − 5 = _____

⑤

    ____ − 8 = _____

⑥

    9 + ____ = 13

Add or subtract.

⑦ 13 – 7 = ☐   ⑧ 8 + 5 = ☐

⑨ 6 + 8 = ☐   ⑩ 11 – 7 = ☐

⑪ 5 + 10 = ☐   ⑫ 12 – 6 = ☐

⑬ 14 – 6 = ☐   ⑭ 8 + 3 = ☐

⑮ 15 – 9 = ☐   ⑯ 7 + 7 = ☐

⑰ 11 – 10 = ☐   ⑱ 15 + 0 = ☐

⑲ 12 + 3 = ☐   ⑳ 15 – 6 = ☐

㉑
$$\begin{array}{r} 4 \\ +\ 9 \\ \hline \end{array}$$

㉒
$$\begin{array}{r} 14 \\ -\ 9 \\ \hline \end{array}$$

㉓
$$\begin{array}{r} 11 \\ +\ 2 \\ \hline \end{array}$$

㉔
$$\begin{array}{r} 12 \\ -\ 10 \\ \hline \end{array}$$

㉕
$$\begin{array}{r} 9 \\ -\ 6 \\ \hline \end{array}$$

㉖
$$\begin{array}{r} 12 \\ -\ 5 \\ \hline \end{array}$$

㉗
$$\begin{array}{r} 13 \\ -\ 11 \\ \hline \end{array}$$

㉘
$$\begin{array}{r} 13 \\ +\ 2 \\ \hline \end{array}$$

㉙
$$\begin{array}{r} 15 \\ -\ 12 \\ \hline \end{array}$$

㉚
$$\begin{array}{r} 6 \\ +\ 8 \\ \hline \end{array}$$

㉛
$$\begin{array}{r} 7 \\ +\ 5 \\ \hline \end{array}$$

㉜
$$\begin{array}{r} 14 \\ -\ 8 \\ \hline \end{array}$$

Complete the tables.

 33

+	4	5	6
7			
8			
9			15

34

13	14	15	−
			7
			8
		6	9

Match.

35

$$15 - 11$$

14 − 9

14 − 11

In each group, colour the two numbers that give the sum in the centre.

36

37

Complete.

�38 Jack has 6 🍭 . Jane has 8 🍭 . How many 🍭 do they have altogether? _____ 🍭 altogether.	6 + 8 ____
�39 Sam has 13 🎈 . Sue has 9 🎈 . How many more 🎈 does Sam have than Sue? _____ more 🎈 .	
�40 There are 14 🐚 and 10 🐚 . How many more 🐚 are there than 🐚 ? _____ more 🐚 .	
�41 There are 5 🐰 and 6 🐰 . How many 🐰 🐰 are there in all? _____ 🐰 🐰 in all.	

Colour the path for Little Ant to get the food.
Start from 0. Count by 5's to 50.

Addition Facts to 20

12   +   8   =   20

HINTS:

Adding means joining two groups or putting two groups together.

Complete each addition sentence.

① _____ + _____ = _____

② _____ + _____ = _____

③ _____ + _____ = _____

④ _____ + _____ = _____

⑤ _____ + _____ = _____

⑥ _____ + _____ = _____

Add.

⑦ $16 + 4 =$ ☐	⑧ $13 + 6 =$ ☐
⑨ $11 + 8 =$ ☐	⑩ $15 + 4 =$ ☐
⑪ $12 + 7 =$ ☐	⑫ $17 + 3 =$ ☐
⑬ $10 + 9 =$ ☐	⑭ $14 + 4 =$ ☐
⑮ $8 + 9 =$ ☐	⑯ $19 + 1 =$ ☐
⑰ $15 + 2 =$ ☐	⑱ $12 + 5 =$ ☐
⑲ $13 + 4 =$ ☐	⑳ $11 + 9 =$ ☐

㉑
$$\begin{array}{r} 17 \\ +\ \ 2 \\ \hline \end{array}$$
☐

㉒
$$\begin{array}{r} 10 \\ +\ \ 8 \\ \hline \end{array}$$
☐

㉓
$$\begin{array}{r} 15 \\ +\ \ 5 \\ \hline \end{array}$$
☐

㉔
$$\begin{array}{r} 12 \\ +\ \ 6 \\ \hline \end{array}$$
☐

㉕
$$\begin{array}{r} 11 \\ +\ \ 5 \\ \hline \end{array}$$
☐

㉖
$$\begin{array}{r} 13 \\ +\ \ 6 \\ \hline \end{array}$$
☐

㉗
$$\begin{array}{r} 14 \\ +\ \ 3 \\ \hline \end{array}$$
☐

㉘
$$\begin{array}{r} 16 \\ +\ \ 3 \\ \hline \end{array}$$
☐

㉙
$$\begin{array}{r} 18 \\ +\ \ 2 \\ \hline \end{array}$$
☐

㉚
$$\begin{array}{r} 9 \\ +\ \ 7 \\ \hline \end{array}$$
☐

㉛
$$\begin{array}{r} 19 \\ +\ \ 1 \\ \hline \end{array}$$
☐

㉜
$$\begin{array}{r} 10 \\ +\ 10 \\ \hline \end{array}$$
☐

Match and complete. Write the letters in ㊽ to solve the riddle.

㉝ $15 + 3 =$ _____   •   • (n) $13 + 3 =$ _____

㉞ $10 + 6 =$ _____   •   • (k) $12 + 2 =$ _____

㉟ $9 + 5 =$ _____   •   • (r) $16 + 2 =$ _____

㊱ $11 + 6 =$ _____   •   • (h) $16 + 4 =$ _____

㊲ $12 + 8 =$ _____   •   • (c) $16 + 1 =$ _____

㊳ $13 + 2 =$ _____   •   • (e) $15 + 4 =$ _____

㊴ $16 + 3 =$ _____   •   • (d) $14 + 1 =$ _____

㊵ $11 + 1 =$ _____   •   • (a) $6 + 5 =$ _____

㊶ $9 + 4 =$ _____   •   • (f) $10 + 2 =$ _____

㊷ $7 + 4 =$ _____   •   • (i) $6 + 7 =$ _____

Riddle: What do you need when you sweat?

㊸

20	11	16	15	14	19	18	17	20	13	19	12
A	h										

Complete.

㊹ There are 10 🎂 and 10 🎂 in the bakery.
How many 🎂 🎂 are there in all?

_____ = _____   _____ 🎂 🎂 in all.

㊺ There are 12 🥧 and 6 🥧 .
How many 🥧 🥧 are there in all?

_____ = _____   _____ 🥧 🥧 in all.

㊻ There are 8 🧁 and 8 🧁 .
How many 🧁 🧁 are there in all?

_____ = _____   _____ 🧁 🧁 in all.

㊼ There are 9 🍞 . The baker makes 10 more 🍞 .
How many 🍞 are there in all?

_____ = _____   _____ 🍞 in all.

㊽ There are 13 ⊙ in ▱ and 4 ⊙ in 📦 .
How many ⊙ are there in all?

_____ = _____   _____ ⊙ in all.

**Colour the path for Sam to get his bike. Start from 10.
Count by 10's to 100.**

10	30	60	70	50
10	40	50	80	90
20	30	60	60	100
10	20	30	70	80

Subtraction Facts to 20

$$17 \quad - \quad 5 \quad = \quad 12$$

HINTS:

Subtracting means taking one group away from another.

Complete each subtraction sentence.

①

$$16 - 8 = \underline{\quad\quad}$$

②

$$\underline{\quad} - \underline{\quad} = \underline{\quad\quad}$$

③

$$\underline{\quad} - \underline{\quad} = \underline{\quad\quad}$$

④

$$\underline{\quad} - \underline{\quad} = \underline{\quad\quad}$$

⑤

$$\underline{\quad} - \underline{\quad} = \underline{\quad\quad}$$

⑥

$$\underline{\quad} - \underline{\quad} = \underline{\quad\quad}$$

Add or subtract.

⑦ 18 − 7 = ☐ ⑧ 16 − 9 = ☐

⑨ 20 − 11 = ☐ ⑩ 19 − 4 = ☐

⑪ 17 − 8 = ☐ ⑫ 18 − 12 = ☐

⑬ 16 − 4 = ☐ ⑭ 20 − 6 = ☐

⑮ 19 − 17 = ☐ ⑯ 17 − 4 = ☐

⑰ 20 − 2 = ☐ ⑱ 16 − 13 = ☐

⑲ 18 − 4 = ☐ ⑳ 17 − 11 = ☐

㉑
$$\begin{array}{r} 19 \\ -3 \\ \hline \end{array}$$
☐

㉒
$$\begin{array}{r} 16 \\ -10 \\ \hline \end{array}$$
☐

㉓
$$\begin{array}{r} 18 \\ -8 \\ \hline \end{array}$$
☐

㉔
$$\begin{array}{r} 17 \\ -5 \\ \hline \end{array}$$
☐

㉕
$$\begin{array}{r} 20 \\ -5 \\ \hline \end{array}$$
☐

㉖
$$\begin{array}{r} 17 \\ -8 \\ \hline \end{array}$$
☐

㉗
$$\begin{array}{r} 16 \\ -9 \\ \hline \end{array}$$
☐

㉘
$$\begin{array}{r} 19 \\ -13 \\ \hline \end{array}$$
☐

㉙
$$\begin{array}{r} 18 \\ -15 \\ \hline \end{array}$$
☐

㉚
$$\begin{array}{r} 16 \\ -12 \\ \hline \end{array}$$
☐

㉛
$$\begin{array}{r} 19 \\ -5 \\ \hline \end{array}$$
☐

㉜
$$\begin{array}{r} 20 \\ -7 \\ \hline \end{array}$$
☐

Subtract. Help Little Bunny go through the forest.

㉝ 16 − 10 = ☐

㉞ 20 − 13 = ☐

㉟
```
   1 8
 −   7
 ─────
   ☐
```

㊲ 16 − 11 = ☐

㊱ 17 − 12 = ☐

㊳
```
   1 6
 − 1 5
 ─────
   ☐
```

㊴ 18 − 16 = ☐

㊵ 19 − 14 = ☐

㊶
```
   1 7
 − 1 5
 ─────
   ☐
```

㊷ 18 − 11 = ☐

㊸
```
   1 9
 − 1 0
 ─────
   ☐
```

㊹ 18 − 6 = ☐

Complete.

㊺ Sue bought 18 ✏. Sam bought 12 ✏.
How many more ✏ did Sue buy than Sam?

_____ = _____ _____ more ✏ .

㊻ Jack has 17 📝. Jane has 9 📝.
How many more 📝 does Jack have than Jane?

_____ = _____ _____ more 📝 .

㊼ Bob has 20 🧱. Ben has 18 🧱.
How many more 🧱 does Bob have than Ben?

_____ = _____ _____ more 🧱 .

㊽ There are 16 🎾 on the table. 5 🎾 roll off.
How many 🎾 are left on the table?

_____ = _____ _____ 🎾 left.

㊾ There are 19 children in the playground. 9 of them are boys.
How many girls are there in the playground?

_____ = _____ _____ girls.

Colour the cards with the same answers.

| 18 − 4 | 12 − 8 | 16 − 11 |

| 19 − 5 | 17 − 4 | 20 − 6 | 14 − 10 |

Addition and Subtraction Facts to 20

EXAMPLES

Sue has 18 ✏ . Sam has 2 ✏ .

1. How many ✏ do they have altogether?

   18 + 2 = 20   20 ✏ altogether.

2. How many more ✏ does Sue have than Sam?

   18 − 2 = 16   16 more ✏ .

HINTS:

Read each question carefully to see if it is an addition or a subtraction problem.

Draw a line to show 2 groups or circle the group to be taken away. Complete each number sentence.

① 16 + _4_ = 20

② 18 − 6 = _12_

③ 12 + ___ = _____

④ ___ − 5 = _____

⑤ ___ − 14 = _____

⑥ 8 + ___ = _____

Add or subtract.

⑦ 18 – 4 = ☐   ⑧ 16 + 3 = ☐

⑨ 15 + 4 = ☐   ⑩ 19 – 12 = ☐

⑪ 12 – 9 = ☐   ⑫ 20 – 8 = ☐

⑬ 17 – 14 = ☐   ⑭ 17 + 2 = ☐

⑮ 16 – 12 = ☐   ⑯ 15 + 5 = ☐

⑰ 19 + 1 = ☐   ⑱ 18 – 11 = ☐

⑲ 20 + 0 = ☐   ⑳ 17 – 9 = ☐

㉑
$$\begin{array}{r} 15 \\ + \ 2 \\ \hline \end{array}$$
☐

㉒
$$\begin{array}{r} 16 \\ - \ 9 \\ \hline \end{array}$$
☐

㉓
$$\begin{array}{r} 17 \\ + \ 3 \\ \hline \end{array}$$
☐

㉔
$$\begin{array}{r} 20 \\ - \ 9 \\ \hline \end{array}$$
☐

㉕
$$\begin{array}{r} 18 \\ - \ 15 \\ \hline \end{array}$$
☐

㉖
$$\begin{array}{r} 16 \\ + \ 4 \\ \hline \end{array}$$
☐

㉗
$$\begin{array}{r} 17 \\ - \ 13 \\ \hline \end{array}$$
☐

㉘
$$\begin{array}{r} 19 \\ - \ 9 \\ \hline \end{array}$$
☐

㉙
$$\begin{array}{r} 20 \\ - \ 4 \\ \hline \end{array}$$
☐

㉚
$$\begin{array}{r} 17 \\ - \ 5 \\ \hline \end{array}$$
☐

㉛
$$\begin{array}{r} 18 \\ + \ 2 \\ \hline \end{array}$$
☐

㉜
$$\begin{array}{r} 15 \\ + \ 3 \\ \hline \end{array}$$
☐

In each group, colour the plates that match the number.

 ㉝ 19   12 + 7   20 − 1   14 + 4   13 + 6

 ㉞ 16   20 − 4   12 + 3   19 − 3   9 + 7

 ㉟ 13   9 + 5   19 − 6   17 − 4   7 + 6

 ㊱ 15   18 − 3   9 + 7   17 − 2   11 + 4

 ㊲ 18   18 − 0   20 − 2   10 + 8   12 + 5

 ㊳ 11   16 − 4   7 + 4   17 − 6   9 + 2

 ㊴ 12   8 + 4   19 − 7   6 + 5   16 − 4

Complete.

㊵ There are 17 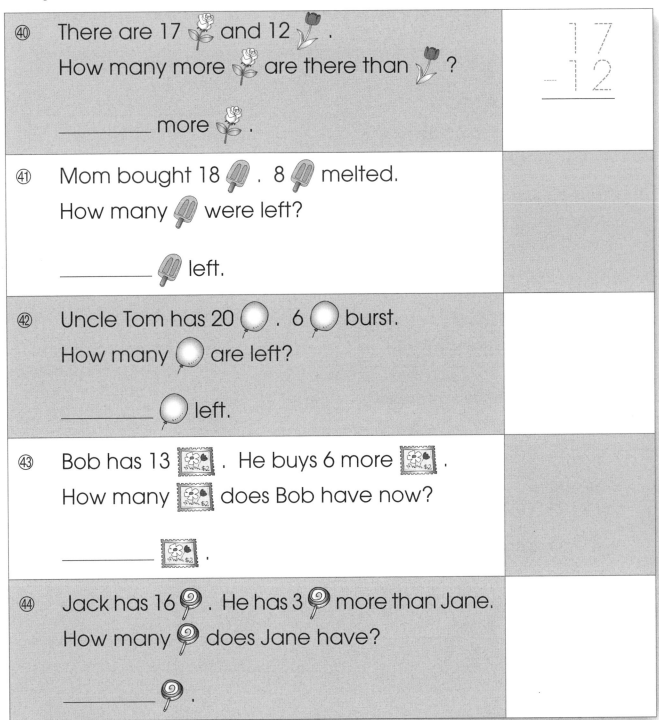 and 12 . How many more are there than ? _____ more .	17 – 12 ––––
㊶ Mom bought 18 . 8 melted. How many were left? _____ left.	
㊷ Uncle Tom has 20 . 6 burst. How many are left? _____ left.	
㊸ Bob has 13 . He buys 6 more . How many does Bob have now? _____ .	
㊹ Jack has 16 . He has 3 more than Jane. How many does Jane have? _____ .	

Put the numbers in the correct counting order, starting with the largest number.

12   48   65   7   32   56   29

___ ___ ___ ___ ___ ___ ___

15 More Addition and Subtraction

1.
goes up by one
goes up by one

$$6 + 6 = 12$$
$$7 + 6 = 13$$
$$8 + 6 = 14$$

goes up by one
goes up by one

2.
goes up by one
goes up by one

$$12 - 7 = 5$$
$$13 - 7 = 6$$
$$14 - 7 = 7$$

goes up by one
goes up by one

Complete the number sentences.

HINTS:

- Knowing the addition or subtraction patterns may help you find the sum or difference faster.

- Using tens may also help you find the sum and difference faster.

  e.g. $7 + 5 = 7 + 3 + 2$
  $$= 10 + 2$$
  $$= 12$$

  $12 - 4 = 10 + 2 - 4$
  $$= 10 - 4 + 2$$
  $$= 6 + 2$$
  $$= 8$$

① $7 + 7 \ = 14$

   a. $8 + 7 \ = \underline{\hphantom{00}}$

   b. $9 + 7 \ = \underline{\hphantom{00}}$

   c. $10 + 7 = \underline{\hphantom{00}}$

   d. $11 + 7 = \underline{\hphantom{00}}$

   e. $12 + 7 = \underline{\hphantom{00}}$

② $8 + 8 \ = 16$

   a. $8 + 9 \ = \underline{\hphantom{00}}$

   b. $8 + 10 = \underline{\hphantom{00}}$

   c. $8 + 11 = \underline{\hphantom{00}}$

   d. $8 + 12 = \underline{\hphantom{00}}$

③ $5 + 5 = 10$

   a. $5 + 6 = \underline{\hphantom{00}}$

   b. $5 + 7 = \underline{\hphantom{00}}$

   c. $5 + 8 = \underline{\hphantom{00}}$

   d. $5 + 9 = \underline{\hphantom{00}}$

④ $18 - 8 = 10$
  a. $18 - 9 = \underline{\quad\quad}$
  b. $18 - 10 = \underline{\quad\quad}$
  c. $18 - 11 = \underline{\quad\quad}$
  d. $18 - 12 = \underline{\quad\quad}$
  e. $18 - 13 = \underline{\quad\quad}$

⑤ $12 - 6 = 6$
  a. $13 - 6 = \underline{\quad\quad}$
  b. $14 - 6 = \underline{\quad\quad}$
  c. $15 - 6 = \underline{\quad\quad}$
  d. $16 - 6 = \underline{\quad\quad}$
  e. $17 - 6 = \underline{\quad\quad}$

Draw and complete.

⑥ $7 + 5$
$= 10 + \underline{2}$
 $= \underline{\quad\quad}$

⑦ $8 + 7$
$= 10 + \underline{\quad}$
$= \underline{\quad\quad}$

⑧ $9 + 4$
$= 10 + \underline{\quad}$
$= \underline{\quad\quad}$

⑨ $6 + 8$
$= 10 + \underline{\quad}$
$= \underline{\quad\quad}$

⑩ $8 + 9$
$= 10 + \underline{\quad}$
$= \underline{\quad\quad}$

⑪ $9 + 6$
$= 10 + \underline{\quad}$
$= \underline{\quad\quad}$

Cross out the correct number of items and complete the subtraction sentences.

⑫

$12 - 4$
$= 10 - \underline{2}$
$= \underline{}$

⑬

$14 - 6$
$= 10 - \underline{}$
$= \underline{}$

⑭

$16 - 9$
$= 10 - \underline{}$
$= \underline{}$

⑮

$13 - 7$
$= 10 - \underline{}$
$= \underline{}$

⑯

$15 - 8$
$= 10 - \underline{}$
$= \underline{}$

⑰

$17 - 9$
$= 10 - \underline{}$
$= \underline{}$

Add.

⑱
```
   2
   4
+  8
```
☐

⑲
```
   3
   2
+  7
```
☐

⑳
```
   7
   2
+  9
```
☐

㉑
```
   8
   0
+  7
```
☐

㉒
```
   9
   1
+  6
```
☐

㉓
```
   5
   5
+  7
```
☐

㉔
```
   2
   8
+  9
```
☐

㉕
```
   3
   7
+  5
```
☐

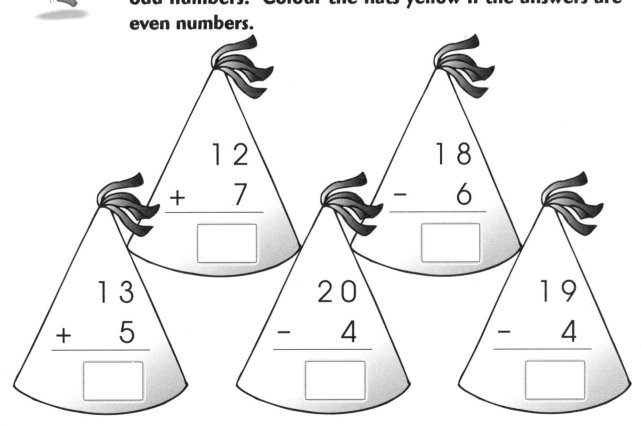

Complete. Colour the party hats red if the answers are odd numbers. Colour the hats yellow if the answers are even numbers.

```
 12
+  7
____
```
☐

```
 18
-  6
____
```
☐

```
 13
+  5
____
```
☐

```
 20
-  4
____
```
☐

```
 19
-  4
____
```
☐

Addition and Subtraction with Money

EXAMPLES

How many cents are there in the piggy bank?

$$5 + 1 + 1 = 7$$

There are 7¢ in the piggy bank.

How many cents are there in each set?

① _____ 4¢

② _____

③ _____

④ _____

HINTS:

- ¢ means cent.
- 1 dime = 10 ¢
- 1 nickel = 5 ¢
- 1 penny = 1 ¢
- Don't forget to add ¢ sign when you add or subtract cents.

The children go to a garage sale. Circle the coins needed to buy each item.

⑤ 4 ¢

⑥ 8 ¢

⑦ 10 ¢

⑧ 5 ¢

How much change do they get?

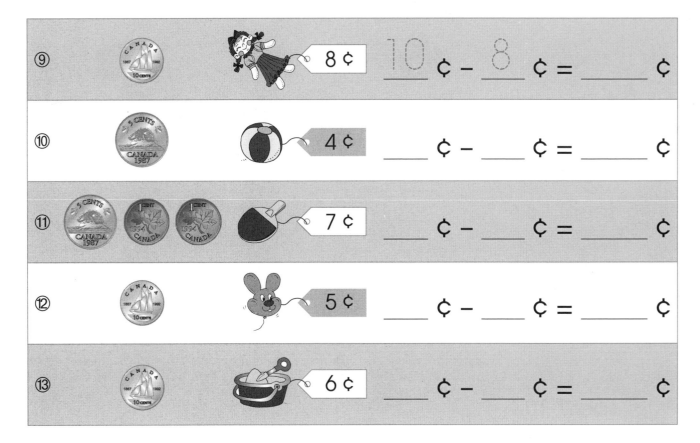

⑨   8 ¢   10 ¢ – 8 ¢ = _____ ¢

⑩   4 ¢   ____ ¢ – ____ ¢ = _____ ¢

⑪   7 ¢   ____ ¢ – ____ ¢ = _____ ¢

⑫   5 ¢   ____ ¢ – ____ ¢ = _____ ¢

⑬   6 ¢   ____ ¢ – ____ ¢ = _____ ¢

How much more do they need?

⑭   8 ¢   8 ¢ – 5 ¢ = _____ ¢

⑮   10 ¢   ____ ¢ – ____ ¢ = _____ ¢

⑯   6 ¢   ____ ¢ – ____ ¢ = _____ ¢

⑰   7 ¢   ____ ¢ – ____ ¢ = _____ ¢

⑱   5 ¢   ____ ¢ – ____ ¢ = _____ ¢

The children spent the exact amounts to buy the garage sale items. Write the letters in the boxes to tell what they bought.

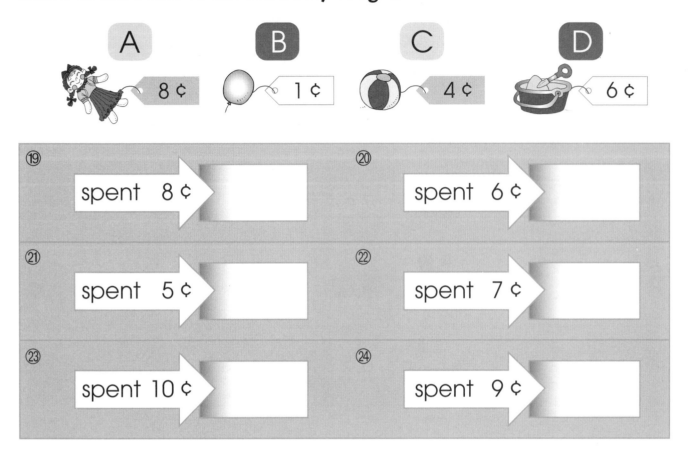

A 8 ¢

B 1 ¢

C 4 ¢

D 6 ¢

⑲ spent 8 ¢

⑳ spent 6 ¢

㉑ spent 5 ¢

㉒ spent 7 ¢

㉓ spent 10 ¢

㉔ spent 9 ¢

Show 3 different ways to make 10¢ with nickels and pennies. Circle the correct number of coins.

Complete.

㉘ Mom buys 1 🍎 and 1 🍐 . How much does she pay in all?

_____ = _____ _____ ¢ in all.

㉙ Sue buys 1 🍇 . Sam buys 1 🍐 . How much more does Sue pay than Sam?

_____ = _____ _____ more ¢.

㉚ Jane buys 1 🍊 and 1 🍌 . How much does Jane pay in all?

_____ = _____ _____ ¢ in all.

㉛ Bob buys 1 🍊 . Ben buys 1 🍎 . How much more does Bob pay than Ben?

_____ = _____ _____ more ¢.

㉜ Jack buys 1 🍌 , 1 🍐 and 1 🍊 . How much does he pay in all?

_____ = _____ _____ ¢ in all.

Just for Fun

Little Frog hops in steps of 2's. Colour the path that he follows.

Final Review

Add or subtract.

①
```
  1 2
+   8
```
[ ]

②
```
  1 8
-   7
```
[ ]

③
```
  1 4
+   4
```
[ ]

④
```
  1 9
-   4
```
[ ]

⑤
```
  1 7
-   4
```
[ ]

⑥
```
  1 1
+   5
```
[ ]

⑦
```
  1 3
+   4
```
[ ]

⑧
```
  1 8
-   8
```
[ ]

⑨
```
  1 4
+   2
```
[ ]

⑩
```
  1 6
-   6
```
[ ]

⑪
```
  2 0
-   6
```
[ ]

⑫
```
  1 7
+   2
```
[ ]

⑬

-9	
20	
17	
15	
18	

⑭

+3	
16	
15	
13	
17	

⑮

-6	
19	
16	
12	
18	

⑯ 8 + 2 + 9 = _____

⑰ 3 + 4 + 6 = _____

Complete and match. Write the letters in ㉖ to solve the riddle.

⑱ 18 – 2 = _____ N   •   • 17 – 2 = _____

⑲ 10 + 4 = _____ A   •   • 7 + 4 = _____

⑳ 8 + 7 = _____ D   •   • 9 + 7 = _____

㉑ 17 – 6 = _____ O   •   • 19 – 5 = _____

㉒ 20 – 7 = _____ U   •   • 16 – 4 = _____

㉓ 5 + 12 = _____ I   •   • 5 + 8 = _____

㉔ 19 – 7 = _____ S   •   • 12 + 6 = _____

㉕ 9 + 9 = _____ R   •   • 20 – 3 = _____

Riddle: A large reptile which is extinct.

㉖

15	17	16	11	12	14	13	18
A							

•

Put + or − in ○ .

㉗ $12\ ○\ 7 = 19$ ㉘ $16\ ○\ 4 = 12$

㉙ $11\ ○\ 6 = 5$ ㉚ $8\ ○\ 3 = 11$

㉛ $13\ ○\ 5 = 18$ ㉜ $15\ ○\ 2 = 13$

㉝ $6\ ○\ 8 = 14$ ㉞ $10\ ○\ 6 = 16$

㉟ $14\ ○\ 5 = 9$ ㊱ $7\ ○\ 6 = 13$

㊲ $18\ ○\ 6 = 12$ ㊳ $13\ ○\ 9 = 4$

Write the numbers.

㊴ $17 - \boxed{}$ ㊵ $2 + \boxed{}$

㊶ $15 - \boxed{}$ ㊷ $5 + \boxed{}$

(7)

㊸ $12 - \boxed{}$ ㊹ $6 + \boxed{}$

㊺ $19 - \boxed{}$ ㊻ $4 + \boxed{}$

Put the sums of the pairs of cards in order, starting with the smallest number first. Write 1st, 2nd, 3rd or 4th in $\boxed{}$ **.**

㊼

| 5 | 9 | | 6 | 5 | | 4 | 8 | | 7 | 6 |

A $\boxed{}$ B $\boxed{}$ C $\boxed{}$ D $\boxed{}$

Complete the number sentences.

⑱
$$6 + 6 = 12$$
a. $6 + 7 = \underline{\hspace{1.5cm}}$
b. $6 + 8 = \underline{\hspace{1.5cm}}$
c. $6 + 9 = \underline{\hspace{1.5cm}}$

⑲
$$14 - 7 = 7$$
a. $15 - 7 = \underline{\hspace{1.5cm}}$
b. $16 - 7 = \underline{\hspace{1.5cm}}$
c. $17 - 7 = \underline{\hspace{1.5cm}}$

Draw and complete.

㊿
$$8 + 5$$
$$= 10 + \underline{\hspace{1cm}}$$
$$= \underline{\hspace{1.5cm}}$$

51
$$7 + 6$$
$$= 10 + \underline{\hspace{1cm}}$$
$$= \underline{\hspace{1.5cm}}$$

Cross out the correct number of items and complete the subtraction sentences.

52
$$13 - 6$$
$$= 10 - \underline{\hspace{1cm}}$$
$$= \underline{\hspace{1.5cm}}$$

53
$$14 - 8$$
$$= 10 - \underline{\hspace{1cm}}$$
$$= \underline{\hspace{1.5cm}}$$

Circle the coins needed to buy each item.

54 9¢

55 7¢

Complete.

56 There are 18 🏐 on the table. 6 🏐 roll off.

How many 🏐 are left on the table?

_____ 🏐 left.

57 There are 6 🥐 in the box. Mom makes 12 more 🥐 .

How many 🥐 are there in all?

_____ 🥐 in all.

58 Sue has 10¢ in all. She buys 1 🏐 5¢ .

How much does Sue have left?

_____ ¢ left.

59 Sam has 6 🎈 and 5 🎈 .

How many 🎈 🎈 does Sam have altogether?

_____ 🎈 🎈 altogether.

60 Bob has 15 🍭 . Ben has 9 🍭 .

How many more 🍭 does Bob have than Ben?

_____ more 🍭 .

61 Jack buys 1 🚗 7¢ . Jane buys 1 ✈️ 9¢ .

How much more does Jane spend than Jack?

_____ ¢ more.

Section III

Overview

In Section II, addition and subtraction skills were developed.

In this section, additional opportunities are provided for children to practise these skills in meaningful contexts.

The concepts of shape and symmetry are also developed. Children learn to recognize 2-dimensional shapes such as rectangle, square, triangle, hexagon and circle, and 3-dimensional shapes such as sphere, prism, cone, cylinder and pyramid.

In addition, topics such as measurement, money and graphs are introduced. At this stage, children should be able to use "mathematical language" to express their thinking.

Comparing, Sorting and Ordering

Write the letters in the ☐ **.**

Hello. My name is Jill. I can see many things in the supermarket.

① A.

B.

Light ☐

Heavy ☐

② A.

B.

Big ☐

Small ☐

③ A.

B.

Thick ☐

Thin ☐

④ A.

B.

Straight ☐

Bent ☐

⑤ A.

B.

Short ☐

Long ☐

⑥ A.

B.

More ☐

Fewer ☐

Circle the right answers.

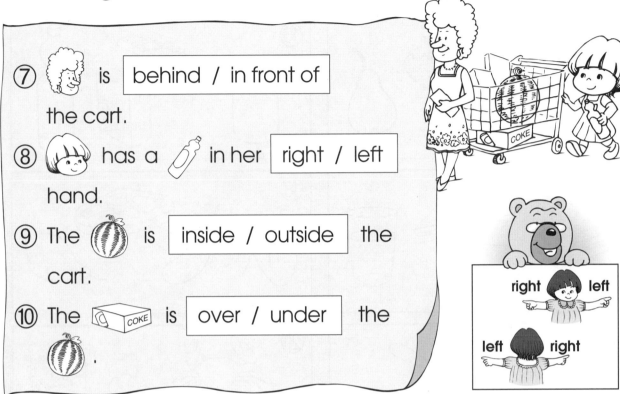

⑦ 🧑 is | behind / in front of | the cart.

⑧ 👧 has a 🍼 in her | right / left | hand.

⑨ The 🍉 is | inside / outside | the cart.

⑩ The 🧃COKE is | over / under | the 🍉 .

Tick ✔ the right ☐ .

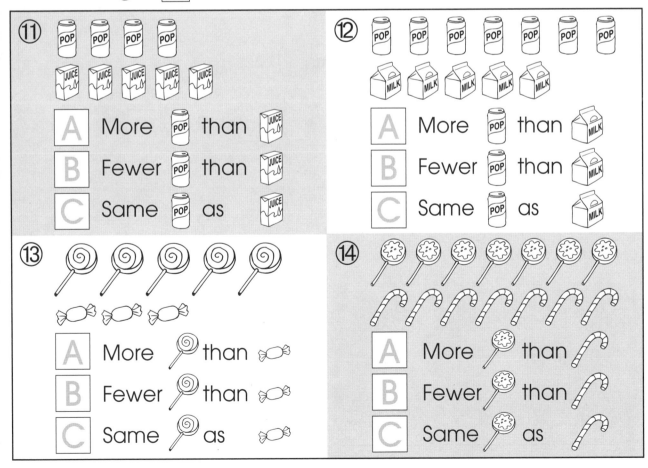

⑪
A	More POP than JUICE
B	Fewer POP than JUICE
C	Same POP as JUICE

⑫
A	More POP than MILK
B	Fewer POP than MILK
C	Same POP as MILK

⑬
A	More 🍭 than 🍬
B	Fewer 🍭 than 🍬
C	Same 🍭 as 🍬

⑭
A	More 🍪 than 🍬
B	Fewer 🍪 than 🍬
C	Same 🍪 as 🍬

Sort the things for Jill. Cross out ✗ the one that does not belong.

Which comes next? Tick ✔ the right ☐ .

Put the things in order.

㉕ From short to long

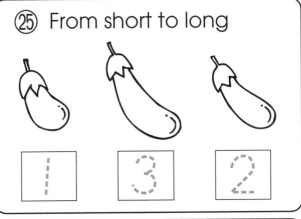

| 1 | 3 | 2 |

㉖ From big to small

㉗ From thin to thick

㉘ From narrow to wide

A C T I V I T Y

Colour the things.

1. Colour the **taller** light **blue**.
2. Colour the **bigger** picture **green**.
3. Colour the puppy **behind** the couch **brown**.
4. Colour the puppy **under** the couch **yellow**.

Numbers 1 - 10

Count and write the numbers.

①

Numbers 1 to 10

• 1	⋮ 2	⋰ 3	⋮⋮ 4
⋮⋮ 5	⋮⋮⋮ 6	⋰⋰ 7	
⋮⋮ 8	⋮⋮⋮ 9	⋮⋮⋮ 10	

②

③

④

Count and colour the bones.

⑤ Colour the even numbers red.

⑥ Colour the odd numbers yellow.

Odd numbers

1	3	5	7	9

Even numbers

2	4	6	8	10

Write the numbers they will walk past.

Count On
Small → Large
e.g. 1, 2, 3, 4, 5 ....
Count Back
Large → Small
e.g. 10, 9, 8, 7, 6 ....

⑦ : 6, ☐ , ☐ , ☐ , 2.

⑧ to : 6, ☐ , ☐ , ☐ , 10.

⑨ to : 10, ☐ , ☐ , ☐ , ☐ , ☐ ,
☐ , ☐ , ☐ , 1.

Circle the right answers.

⑩ 🧸 🐰 ⚽ is in the 2nd 🚃 .

⑪ 🐱 ⚽ 🐰 is in the 5th 🚃 .

→ 🍎 🍐 🍐 🍇 🍌 🍒
The **2nd** and the
3rd are pears.
There are 2 pears.

⑫ 🎾 🐱 💐 is in the 8th 🚃 .

⑬ How many 🚃 are there?   7   8   9 .

Count and write the numbers.

⑭ [ ] and [ ] makes [ ]

"And" means plus. Join the groups to find the total.

⑮ [ ] and [ ] makes [ ]

⑯ [ ] and [ ] makes [ ]

⑰ [ ] and [ ] makes [ ]

⑱ [ ] and [ ] makes [ ]

⑲ take away [ ] leaves [ ]
[ ] take away [ ] leaves [ ]

⑳ [ ] take away [ ] leaves [ ]

3 take away 1 leaves 2. "Take away" means minus.

㉑ [ ] minus [ ] equals [ ]

㉒ [ ] minus [ ] equals [ ]

ACTIVITY

Colour the even numbers red and the odd numbers yellow.

4 1 3 10 2 5 9 7 6 8

3 Addition and Subtraction

How many stars are there?

 and

①   2   +   3   = ☐

 and ☆☆☆

②   ☐   +   ☐   = ☐

☆☆☆
☆☆ and ☆☆

③   ☐   +   ☐   = ☐

Numbers must align on the right-hand side, e.g.

  2
+ 3 ✗   + 3 ✓
 5   5

④   5 ☆☆☆☆☆
   + 1 ☆
   ☐

⑤   2 ☆☆
   + 6 ☆☆☆☆☆☆
   ☐

⑥   4
  + 5
  ☐

⑦   1
  + 6
  ☐

⑧   2
  + 5
  ☐

⑨   6
  + 3
  ☐

⑩ 1 + 9 = ☐

⑪ 5 + 5 = ☐

⑫ 2 + 8 = ☐

⑬ 6 + 4 = ☐

⑭ 9 + 1 = ☐

⑮ 7 + 3 = ☐

Jill and Mark are counting the stars. Write the numbers.

16. 1 ☆
     2 ☆☆
   + 4 ☆☆☆☆
     ☐

17. 2 ☆☆
     3 ☆☆☆
   + 3 ☆☆☆
     ☐

18. 4 ☆☆☆☆
     1 ☆
   + 1 ☆
     ☐

19. 3
     3
   + 1
     ☐

20. 2
     3
   + 4
     ☐

21. 3
     1
   + 4
     ☐

22. 5
     3
   + 2
     ☐

23. **The ☆'s with 6 as the answer are Jill's. Colour them red.**

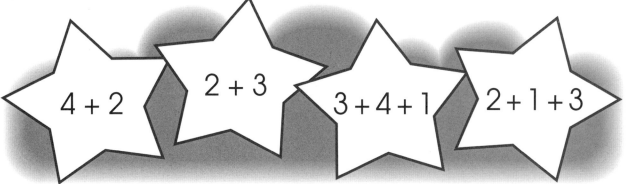

How many Christmas crackers are left?

㉔   7   -   4   =   ☐

㉕   5   -   ☐   =   ☐

㉖   8
  -   6
  ☐

㉗   10
  - ☐
  ☐

㉘   6
  - ☐
  ☐

Try these.

Numbers must align on the right-hand side, e.g.

$$\begin{array}{r} 5 \\ -\ 3 \\ \hline 2 \end{array} ✗ \qquad \begin{array}{r} 5 \\ -\ 3 \\ \hline 2 \end{array} ✓$$

㉙   7
  - 6
  ☐

㉚   10
  - 7
  ☐

㉛   9
  - 5
  ☐

㉜   8
  - 4
  ☐

㉝   6
  - 5
  ☐

㉞   10
  - 2
  ☐

㉟   7
  - 3
  ☐

㊱ 7 - 2 = ☐

㊲ 8 - 2 = ☐

㊳ 9 - 4 = ☐

㊴ 8 - 1 = ☐

㊵ 5 - 1 = ☐

㊶ 6 - 4 = ☐

Read what they say. Write the numbers.

42 I have 5 🧸 . Mom gave me 2 🧸 .

Now I have ⬜ 🧸 .

43 I have 2 red ⬤ and 2 blue ⬤ .

I have ⬜ ⬤ in all.

44 I have 8 🟦 . I gave 2 to 👧 . Now I

have ⬜ 🟦 .

45 👧 has 9 📖 . I have 5 📖 .

👧 has ⬜ 📖 more than me.

46 We had 7 🎈 but 3 🎈 burst.

Now we have ⬜ 🎈 left.

A C T I V I T Y

Which pairs of numbers make 10? Colour them in the same colour.

| 6 | 3 | | 8 | 1 |
| 9 | 2 | | 7 | 4 |

Numbers 11 - 20

Count and write the number of toys. Circle the right words.

① [ ] even / odd

② [ ] even / odd

③ [ ] even / odd

④ [ ] even / odd

A number ending in 0, 2, 4, 6 or 8 is an even number.

A number ending in 1, 3, 5, 7 or 9 is an odd number.

Help Jill throw the balls. Write the numbers.

11 17 16 13 14 15 19 20 18

⑤ Odd Numbers

⑥ Even Numbers

12

Fill in the numbers.

⑦ Count on — 12, ___, 14, ___, ___, ___

⑧ Count back — ___, 18, 17, ___, ___, ___

⑨ Count back / Even Numbers — ___, ___, 14, ___, ___, 8

⑩ Count on / Odd Numbers — ___, 9, ___, ___, 15, ___

Tick ✔ the gifts.

⑪ My gift's number is 5 more than 7.
○ gift   ○ flower   ○ teddy bear

⑫ My gift's number is 4 more than 10.
○ pencil   ○ gift   ○ flower

⑬ My gift's number is 5 less than 12.
○ teddy bear   ○ flower   ○ pencil

teddy bear 12   gift 14
flower 6   pencil 7

5 more than 7
Count on
7 8 9 10 11 12

5 less than 12
Count back
7 8 9 10 11 12

Help Jill draw the lines. Write the numbers.

1 group of 10, 1 group of 5.

⑭ $15 = 10 + 5$

⑮ $15 = \boxed{} + 3$

⑯ $\boxed{} = 8 + \boxed{}$

⑰ $17 = 6 + \boxed{}$

⑱ $\boxed{} = \boxed{} + 9$

⑲ $\boxed{} = 10 + \boxed{}$

⑳ $\boxed{} = 4 + \boxed{}$

Write the numbers.

  Find how much food we had.

Any number plus 0 equals itself.
e.g.

$$5 + 0 = \underline{5}$$

㉑

| 8 |
| 8 |

| 8 | + | 8 | = | | | + | | |

㉒

| | + | | = | | | + | | |

㉓ Oh! No one brought .

| | + | 0 | = | | | + | 0 |

㉔

| | + | | = | | | + | | |

㉕ Oh! No one brought , either.

| | + | 0 | = | | | + | | |

Write the numbers.

Find how much is left.

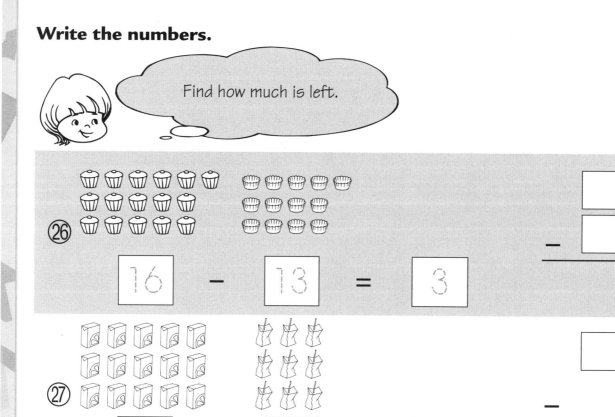

㉖

$$16 - 13 = 3$$

㉗

☐ − ☐ = ☐

㉘

☐ − ☐ = ☐

㉙

☐ − ☐ = ☐

㉚

☐ − ☐ = ☐

Read what Jill and Mark say. Write the numbers.

I have 2 ⓢ.
He has 3 ⓢ.
We have
2 + 3 = [5] ⓢ.

I have 3 ⓢ.
She has 2 ⓢ.
We have
3 + 2 = [5] ⓢ.

Even if the order of addition changes, the answer is the same.

[2] + [3] = [3] + [2]

㉛ 3 + 4 = [ ] + 3

㉜ 5 + [ ] = 2 + 5

㉝ [ ] + 1 = 1 + 8

㉞ 1 + 4 = [ ] + 1

㉟ 3 + [ ] = 1 + 3

㊱ 2 + 6 = 6 + [ ]

ACTIVITY

Write the missing numbers.

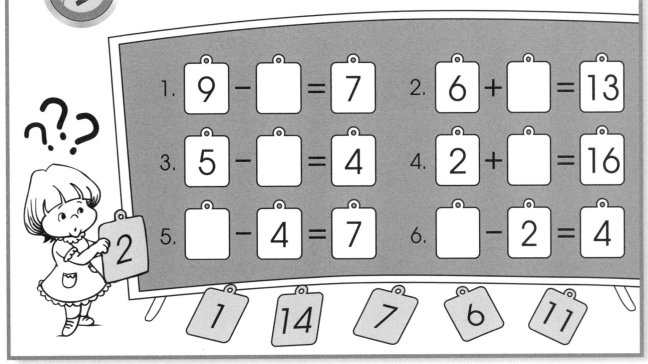

1. 9 − [ ] = 7

2. 6 + [ ] = 13

3. 5 − [ ] = 4

4. 2 + [ ] = 16

5. [ ] − 4 = 7

6. [ ] − 2 = 4

1   14   7   6   11

5 Shapes

Put Jill's things in the right boxes. Write the letters only.

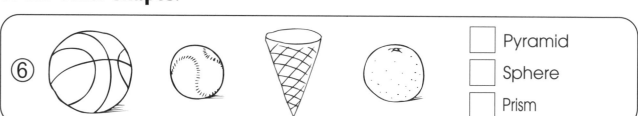

Sphere	Cone	Prism	Cylinder	Pyramid
①	②	③	④	⑤

In each group, circle the shape that is not the same. Tick ✔ the name of the other shapes.

⑥
☐ Pyramid
☐ Sphere
☐ Prism

⑦
☐ Cylinder
☐ Prism
☐ Cone

⑧
☐ Cone
☐ Sphere
☐ Cylinder

⑨ ☐ Cylinder ☐ Cone ☐ Pyramid

⑩ ☐ Sphere ☐ Cone ☐ Cylinder

Colour the shapes.

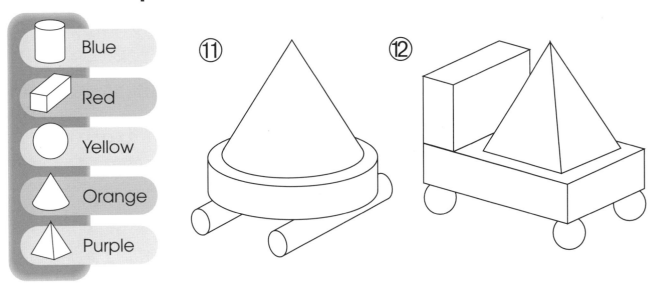

Blue

Red

Yellow

Orange

Purple

⑪

⑫

ACTIVITY

Colour the one that would stand.

1.

2.

3.

4.

Solid Column Graphs

Jill and Mark are building towers. Circle the right answers.

① How many blocks does have?   6   7   9

② How many blocks does have?   7   8   9

③ Whose tower has more blocks?

④ How many more blocks?   1   2   3

Sort Jill's beads by colour. Draw them on the posts.

Cross out ✗ each bead as you draw it.

⑤
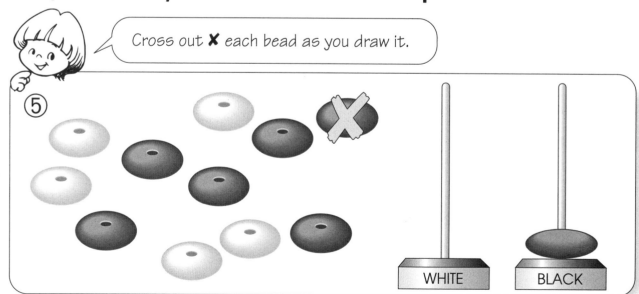

WHITE   BLACK

Write the answers.

⑥ How many ⬛ ? ☐

⑦ How many ⚪ ? ☐

⑧ Which post has more beads? ☐

⑨ How many more? ☐

Tick ✔ the right answers.

Our Grandmas are knitting scarves.

Mrs White

Mrs Lee

Mrs Stanley

⑩ Who has knitted the longest scarf?
☐ Mrs White ☐ Mrs Lee ☐ Mrs Stanley

⑪ Who has knitted the shortest scarf?
☐ Mrs White ☐ Mrs Lee ☐ Mrs Stanley

⑫ How much longer is Mrs Lee's scarf than Mrs Stanley's?
☐ 1 square ☐ 2 squares ☐ 3 squares

⑬ How many more squares must Mrs White knit to catch up to Mrs Lee?
☐ 1 square ☐ 2 squares ☐ 3 squares

Jill, Mark and David go fishing. Fill in the ▢ .

⑭ 👧 has [   ] 🐟 .

⑮ 👦 has [   ] 🐟 .

⑯ 👦 has [   ] 🐟 .

Jill   David   Mark

⑰ They have [   ] 🐟 in all.

⑱ Jill has as many 🐟 as [   ] .

⑲ Mark has more 🐟 than [   ] . He has [   ] more.

⑳ Who has the fewest 🐟 ? [   ]

The graph shows the number of balls the children have. Fill in the ▢.

Jill   Mark   David   Nancy

㉑ has ☐ balls.

㉒ has ☐ balls.

㉓ ☐ has the most balls.

㉔ ☐ has the fewest balls.

㉕ ☐ and ☐ have the same number of balls.

㉖ The children have ☐ balls in all.

ACTIVITY

Complete the graph and answer the questions.

1. Colour 1 box for one child.

2. How many girls? ☐

3. How many boys? ☐

4. How many children? ☐

5. How many more boys than girls? ☐

7 Numbers 20 - 100

Look at the lockers. Do questions 1 to 4.

① Write the missing numbers.

② has a [doll] on her locker door. Her locker number is

[ ] .

③ [face] has a [cat] on his locker door. His locker number is

[ ] .

④ Write from large to small the numbers of the opened lockers:

[ ] , 97 , [ ] , [ ] , 79 , [ ] .

Fill in the missing numbers.

⑤ [ ] 38 [ ] [ ] 41 [ ] [ ]

⑥ [ ] 25 [ ] [ ] 22 [ ] [ ]

⑦ [ ] [ ] 48 49 [ ] [ ] [ ]

⑧ 92 [ ] [ ] [ ] [ ] 87 [ ]

Count and write the numbers.

⑨ +

[2] tens + [4] ones = [24]

The digit in the ones place is any number less than ten, e.g.

23 =

2 tens 3 ones

⑩ + [ ] tens + [ ] ones = [ ]

⑪ + [ ] tens + [ ] ones = [ ]

⑫ + [ ] tens + [ ] ones = [ ]

Circle the better estimates. Count and write how many.

⑬

more than 30
fewer than 30
[ ]

⑭

more than 40
fewer than 40
[ ]

⑮

more than 50
fewer than 50
[ ]

⑯

more than 60
fewer than 60
[ ]

Circle the marbles in groups of ten. Write the numbers.

⑰ | 23 | twenty-three |

⑱ [ ] [ ]

⑲ [ ] [ ]

⑳ [ ] [ ]

Count the blocks. Draw the beads and write the numbers.

㉑ $= 30 + \boxed{5} = $

tens	ones
3	5

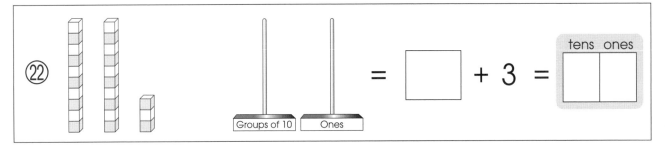

㉒ $= \boxed{} + 3 = $

tens	ones

㉓ $= 60 + \boxed{} = $

tens	ones

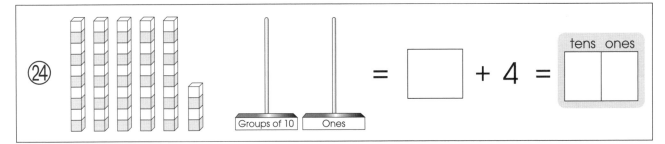

㉔ $= \boxed{} + 4 = $

tens	ones

Colour the even numbers yellow and the odd numbers green.

㉕

62   30   66
21   55   95
44   49   53
37   86

If the last digit of a number is 1,3,5,7 or 9, it is an odd number. If it is 2,4, 6,8 or 0, it is an even number.

Fill in the ☐ **.**

㉖ 36 = ☐ tens and ☐ ones = ☐ + 6

㉗ 49 = ☐ tens and ☐ ones = ☐ + 9

㉘ 61 = ☐ tens and ☐ ones = 60 + ☐

㉙ 75 = ☐ tens and ☐ ones = 70 + ☐

㉚ 90 = ☐ tens and ☐ ones = 90 + ☐

㉛ 9 = ☐ tens and ☐ ones = ☐ + 9

Count the ♥ by 5's and 10's. Write the numbers.

㉜ Count by 5's

5, 10, ☐ , ☐ , ☐ , ☐ ,

☐ , 40, ☐ , ☐ , ☐ , ☐ .

㉝ Count by 10's

10, 20, ☐ , ☐ , ☐ , ☐ .

㉞ Circle the faster way to count.

by 5's   by 10's

Count the flowers in 2's, 5's and 10's. Write the numbers.

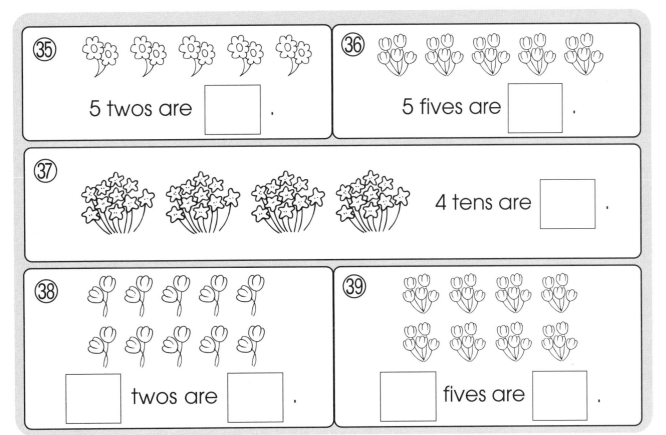

(35) 5 twos are ☐ .

(36) 5 fives are ☐ .

(37) 4 tens are ☐ .

(38) ☐ twos are ☐ .

(39) ☐ fives are ☐ .

ACTIVITY

Count by 10's. Colour the stones that Jill can step on to cross the river.

10
+10 ↓
20
+10 ↓
30
+10 ↓
⋮

95
70
25
85
100
5
10
75
20
80
50
70
90
30
50
40
25
60
100
45
35
40
50
80

Write the letters. (2 marks)

① A. Long ☐
   B. Short ☐

② A. Heavy ☐
   B. Light ☐

Cross out ✗ the thing that is different. (4 marks)

③ ☐ ☐ ☐ ☐
④ ☐ ☐ ☐ ☐
⑤ ☐ ☐ ☐ ☐
⑥ ☐ ☐ ☐ ☐

Which comes next? Circle the right pictures. (2 marks)

⑦

⑧

Circle the right children. (6 marks)

⑨ Who is the 1st?

⑩ Who is the 3rd?

⑪ Who is the 5th?

Write the numbers. (38 marks)

⑫ ☐ + ☐ = ☐   ⑬ ☐ – ☐ = ☐

⑭ ☐ + ☐ + ☐ = ☐

⑮   17
  – 4
  ☐

⑯   8
  – 8
  ☐

⑰   15
  + 0
  ☐

⑱   2
     2
  + 5
  ☐

⑲   1
     4
  + 2
  ☐

⑳   3
     1
  + 4
  ☐

㉑ 9 + 2 = ☐

㉒ 16 – 2 = ☐

㉓ 13 + 6 = ☐

㉔ 2 + 12 = ☐

㉕ 15 – 4 = ☐

㉖ 17 – 17 = ☐

㉗ has 5 🏀 . 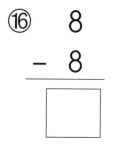 has 13 🏀 .
They have ☐ 🏀 in all.

㉘ 15 boys and 9 girls are in the playground.
There are ☐ more boys.

㉙ There were 14 🌼 in the vase. 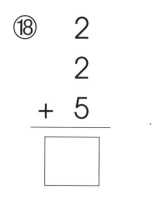 put in 2 more 🌼 .
There are ☐ 🌼 in the vase now.

㉚ has 5 🍦. has 5 🍦 and has 5 🍦.
They have ☐ 🍦 in all.

Write the letters. (8 marks)

A. pyramid   B. sphere   C. cone
D. cylinder   E. prism

㉛   ㉜   ㉝

㉞   ㉟   ㊱

㊲   ㊳

Colour the correct number of **and fill in the** ☐ . **(4 marks)**

㊴ has 5 . has 8 and has 6 .

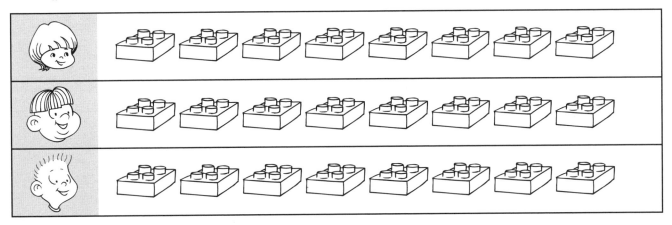

㊵ has ☐ more than .

How many beads? Count and write. (4 marks)

㊶ There are ☐ white beads.

㊷ There are ☐ black beads.

㊸ There are ☐ more white beads.

㊹ There are ☐ beads in all.

Write A for even numbers and B for odd numbers. (10 marks)

㊺ 75 ☐   ㊻ 92 ☐

㊼ 39 ☐   ㊽ 67 ☐

㊾ twenty-eight ☐   ㊿ thirteen ☐

㊿⑤ seventy-one ☐   52 forty-four ☐

53 sixty ☐   54 ninety-six ☐

Write the numbers from the largest to the smallest. (4 marks)

55 52   26   17   43   40   50

☐ , ☐ , ☐ , ☐ , ☐ , ☐

56 36   29   15   41   30   20

☐ , ☐ , ☐ , ☐ , ☐ , ☐

Write the missing numbers. (12 marks)

57 39 = ☐ + 9

58 62 = ☐ + 2

59 99 = 90 + ☐

60 30 = 30 + ☐

61 86 = ☐ + 6

62 14 = ☐ + 4

63 5 = ☐ + 5

64 80 = ☐ + 0

65 4 + 5 = ☐ + 4

66 8 + 9 = ☐ + 8

67 9 + 4 = 4 + ☐

68 ☐ + 6 = 6 + 5

Continue the patterns. (6 marks)

69 40, 50, 60, ☐ , ☐ , ☐ .

70 65, 70, 75, ☐ , ☐ , ☐ .

71 13, 15, 17, ☐ , ☐ , ☐ .

72 35, 40, 45, ☐ , ☐ , ☐ .

73 68, 70, 72, ☐ , ☐ , ☐ .

74 54, 56, 58, ☐ , ☐ , ☐ .

SCORE
100

More about Addition and Subtraction

Help Jill count her toys. Write the numbers in the ☐ **.**

$$25 + 13 = 38$$

Adding 2-digit numbers:

1st add the ones column

2nd add the tens column

$$\begin{array}{r} 2\;5 \\ +\,1\;3 \\ \hline \end{array}$$ **1st** ☐☐

$$\begin{array}{r} 2\boxed{5} \\ +\,1\boxed{3} \\ \hline \end{array}$$ ☐8 **2nd**

$$\begin{array}{r} \boxed{2}5 \\ +\boxed{1}3 \\ \hline \end{array}$$ 38

①

$$32 + 11 = \boxed{}$$

$$\begin{array}{r} 3\;2 \\ +\,1\;1 \\ \hline \end{array}$$

Numbers must align on the right-hand side, e.g.

$$\begin{array}{r} 3\,2 \\ +1\,1 \\ \hline 4\,3 \end{array}\;✗ \qquad \begin{array}{r} 3\,2 \\ +\,1\,1 \\ \hline 4\,3 \end{array}\;✔$$

②

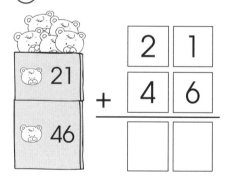

21

46

$$\begin{array}{r} 2\;1 \\ +\,4\;6 \\ \hline \end{array}$$

③

8

70

$$\begin{array}{r} \diagdown\;8 \\ +\,7\;0 \\ \hline \end{array}$$

Put the numbers in the right columns. Tens to tens, and ones to ones.

$$\begin{array}{r} 8 \\ +7\,0 \\ \hline 7\,8 \end{array}\;✗ \qquad \begin{array}{r} \;\;8 \\ +\,7\,0 \\ \hline 7\,8 \end{array}\;✔$$

Try these.

④ $32 + 46 = \boxed{}$

⑤ $28 + 51 = \boxed{}$

⑥ $62 + 5 = \boxed{}$

⑦ $35 + 24 = \boxed{}$

Help Jill count the fruit she picked. Write the numbers in the ☐ .

25	+	17	=	3	12	=	4 2

25		2 5		2 5
+ 17	➡	+ 1 7	➡	+ 1 7
		12		4 2

1st Add the ones.
5 + 7 = 12

2nd 12 = 1 ten + 2 ones
Carry 1 to the tens column.

3rd Leave 2 in the ones column
and add the tens.

⑧

+ 🍐🍐🍐🍐🍐
🍐🍐🍐🍐

= tens ones ☐☐ = ☐

	3	4
+	2	9

Try these.

⑨
	2	8
+	5	6

⑩
	3	7
+	4	9

⑪
	1	2
+	7	8

Write "0" in the ones column when the ones add to 10.

⑫ 9 + 55 = ☐   ⑬ 67 + 8 = ☐

⑭ 18 + 18 = ☐   ⑮ 27 + 13 = ☐

Count the apples and write the numbers in the ☐ .

⑯
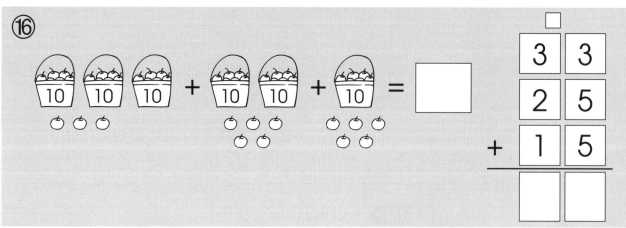

	☐	
	3	3
	2	5
+	1	5

⑰

	☐	
	1	5
		8
+	2	3

⑱

	☐	
	1	6
	1	9
+	3	6

If there are 2 groups of tens, then carry 2 to the tens column.

Try these.

⑲
	☐	
	1	2
	2	3
+	2	7

⑳
	☐	
	3	2
		7
+	2	6

㉑
	☐	
	1	9
	2	8
+	1	9

㉒
	☐	
	1	6
	2	7
+	3	8

㉓
	☐	
	4	6
	2	8
+		9

㉔
	☐	
	3	7
	2	7
+		7

Jill gave Nancy some of her beads. Help her count the beads left. Write the numbers in the ☐ .

㉕

$$\boxed{48} - \boxed{15} = \boxed{}$$

$$\begin{array}{r} 4\ 8 \\ -\ 1\ 5 \\ \hline \end{array}$$

㉖

$$\boxed{} - \boxed{} = \boxed{}$$

Try these.

㉗
$$\begin{array}{r} 3\ 6 \\ -\ 1\ 4 \\ \hline \end{array}$$

㉘
$$\begin{array}{r} 5\ 8 \\ -\ 1\ 6 \\ \hline \end{array}$$

㉙
$$\begin{array}{r} 7\ 7 \\ -\ 5\ 4 \\ \hline \end{array}$$

Don't forget to write "0" under the ones column, e.g.

$$\begin{array}{r} 3\ 8 \\ -\ \ \ 8 \\ \hline 3\ 0 \end{array}$$ You have to write "0" here.

㉚
$$\begin{array}{r} 8\ 6 \\ -\ 7\ 1 \\ \hline \end{array}$$

㉛
$$\begin{array}{r} 6\ 5 \\ -\ 4\ 5 \\ \hline \end{array}$$

㉜
$$\begin{array}{r} 4\ 9 \\ -\ 3\ 2 \\ \hline \end{array}$$

If the first number is zero, you can leave it out. e.g.

$$\begin{array}{r} 3\ 8 \\ -\ 3\ 0 \\ \hline \ \ \ 8 \end{array}$$ Leave it out.

㉝
$$\begin{array}{r} 5\ 2 \\ -\ 5\ 0 \\ \hline \end{array}$$

㉞
$$\begin{array}{r} 1\ 2 \\ -\ 1\ 2 \\ \hline \end{array}$$

㉟
$$\begin{array}{r} 3\ 6 \\ -\ 3\ 0 \\ \hline \end{array}$$

㊱
$$\begin{array}{r} 3\ 8 \\ -\ 3\ 8 \\ \hline \end{array}$$

Read what the children say. Write the equations.

③⑦ There are 13 [girl] and 16 [boy] in my class. How many children are there?

☐ + ☐ = ☐

There are ☐ [girl] and [boy] in all.

+ _____

③⑧ There are 36 [girl] , 21 [boy] and 16 [child] in the playground. How many children are there?

☐ + ☐ + ☐ = ☐

There are ☐ children.

+ _____

③⑨ Our teacher bought us 39 [POP] . We drank 29 [POP] . How many [POP] were left?

☐ − ☐ = ☐

☐ [POP] were left.

− _____

ACTIVITY

Write the answers in the ☐ . Link the people with the same number.

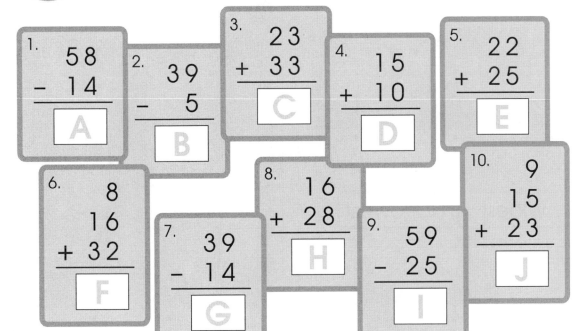

1.
$$58 - 14$$
A

2.
$$39 - 5$$
B

3.
$$23 + 33$$
C

4.
$$15 + 10$$
D

5.
$$22 + 25$$
E

6.
$$8 \\ 16 \\ + 32$$
F

7.
$$39 - 14$$
G

8.
$$16 + 28$$
H

9.
$$59 - 25$$
I

10.
$$9 \\ 15 \\ + 23$$
J

11.

Measurement

Match the words to the pictures.

Widest   Narrowest

Longest   Shortest

Thickest   Thinnest

Heaviest   Lightest

Tallest   Shortest

I can measure with my thumb or a paper clip.

How many thumbs and paper clips? Write the numbers.

⑥ Eraser

⑦ GLUE

⑧

⑨

⑩ Circle the shorter unit.   A.   B.

How long are they ? Write the answers in the ☐ .

To measure accurately, we use a ruler or a measuring tape.
Each mark is 1 centimetre (cm).

CM 0 1 2 3 4 5 6 7 8 9 10 11 12 13 14 15

⑪ ☐ cm

⑫ ☐ cm

⑬ ☐ cm

☐ cm

"cm" is short for centimetre.

When you measure something, remember to start from "0".

⑭ ☐ cm

⑮ ☐ cm

Sometimes we can't get exact readings. Measure these worms.

Tick ✔ the right answers.

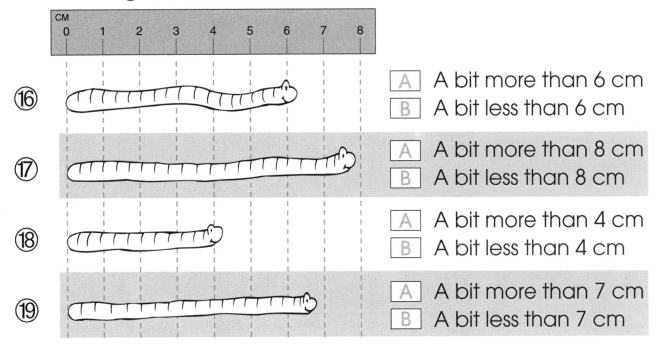

⑯ | A | A bit more than 6 cm
B | A bit less than 6 cm

⑰ | A | A bit more than 8 cm
B | A bit less than 8 cm

⑱ | A | A bit more than 4 cm
B | A bit less than 4 cm

⑲ | A | A bit more than 7 cm
B | A bit less than 7 cm

Estimate and count. Write the numbers.

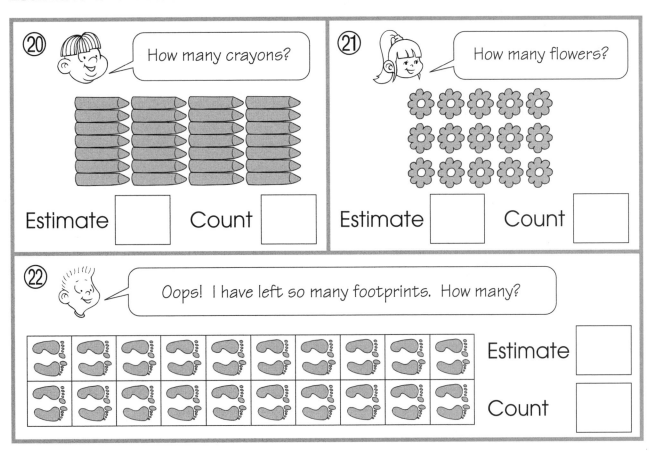

⑳ How many crayons?

Estimate ☐   Count ☐

㉑ How many flowers?

Estimate ☐   Count ☐

㉒ Oops! I have left so many footprints. How many?

Estimate ☐

Count ☐

Colour the reasonable pictures.

㉓

㉔

㉕

In each group, colour the one that holds the most water.

㉖

㉗

㉘

Fill in the blanks.

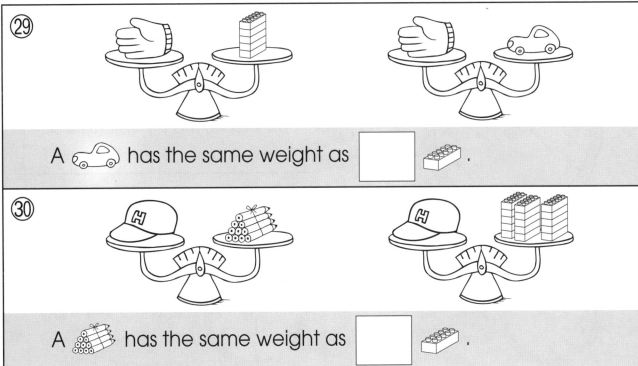

㉙ A 🚗 has the same weight as ☐ 🧱.

㉚ A 🪵 has the same weight as ☐ 🧱.

A C T I V I T Y

Measure and colour.

Measure with your 👍 thumb or a 📏 ruler.

1. Colour the shortest path from 🏠 to 🍦 yellow.

2. Colour the shortest path from 🏰 to 📖 green.

10 Time

Jill has a new clock. Read what she says.

The long hand is the minute hand.
The short hand is the hour hand.

It is <u>three o'clock</u> when the hour hand points to 3 and the minute hand points to 12.

It is <u>half-past two</u> when the hour hand is between 2 and 3 and the minute hand points to 6.

Help Jill write the times.

①

☐ o'clock

②

☐ o'clock

③

☐ o'clock

④

half-past ☐

⑤

half-past ☐

⑥

half-past ☐

Draw the clock hands.

⑦

I wake up at seven o'clock in the morning.

⑧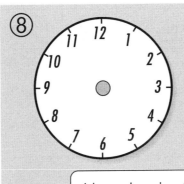

I have lunch at half-past twelve.

⑨

I go home at half-past three.

Tick ✔ the right answers.

The minute hand is <u>past</u> 12. It is <u>a little after</u> 3 o'clock.

The minute hand <u>has not reached</u> 6. It is <u>nearly</u> half-past 9.

⑩

A nearly

B a little after

half-past 3

⑪

A nearly

B a little after

8 o'clock

⑫

A nearly

B a little after

half-past 12

⑬

A nearly

B a little after

2 o'clock

See what Jill will do next week. Fill in the blanks.

Sunday	Monday	Tuesday	Wednesday	Thursday	Friday	Saturday

⑭ When will Jill go to ?

⑮ When will Jill play ?

⑯ When will Jill go to ?

⑰ When will Jill go to ?

⑱ There are ☐ days in a week.

Sunday is the first day of a week.

Saturday is the last day of a week.

Look at Jill's calendar. Colour the months that match the seasons.

January	February	March	April	May	June

July	August	September	October	November	December

⑲ Colour winter ❄ blue. ⑳ Colour spring 🌼 green.

㉑ Colour summer ☀ red. ㉒ Colour fall 🍁 yellow.

Tick ✔ the temperature that matches the season.

㉓ Winter

    A Coldest   B Warmest   C Getting colder

㉔ Spring

    A Warmest   B Getting warmer   C Getting colder

㉕ Summer

    A Getting warmer   B Warmest   C Coldest

㉖ Fall

    A Getting warmer   B Coldest   C Getting colder

See what Jill did last year.

㉗ Put the seasons in order starting with winter.

ACTIVITY

Write the missing dates and do the colouring.

AUGUST

Sunday	Monday	Tuesday	Wednesday	Thursday	Friday	Saturday
	1	2				
7			10			
14			17	18	19	
	22				26	27
28	29	30	31			

1. Colour the day after August 14 red.
2. Colour the day before August 27 green.
3. Colour the third Wednesday yellow.

Money

Match the coins to the value.

① Dime •

• 25¢

② Loonie •

• 10¢

③ Quarter •

• $1

④ Toonie •

• 1¢

⑤ Nickel •

• $2

⑥ Penny •

• 5¢

¢ means cent,
$ means dollar.

Cross out ✗ the coins you count and write the numbers.

⑦ How many pennies? ☐

⑧ How many nickels? ☐

⑨ How many dimes? ☐

⑩ How many quarters? ☐

⑪ How many loonies? ☐

⑫ How many toonies? ☐

How much is each coin worth? Tick ✔ the right answer.

⑬
- [ ] A more than 20¢
- [ ] B less than 20¢

⑭
- [ ] A more than 20¢
- [ ] B less than 20¢

⑮
- [ ] A more than 20¢
- [ ] B less than 20¢

⑯
- [ ] A more than 20¢
- [ ] B less than 20¢

⑰
- [ ] A more than 20¢
- [ ] B less than 20¢

⑱
- [ ] A more than 20¢
- [ ] B less than 20¢

Tick ✔ the coins to match the value of the coin on the left.

Write how much each child has.

㉗ Circle the child who has most money.

1 quarter	=	25¢
1 dime	=	10¢
1 nickel	=	5¢
1 penny	=	1¢

Pay with the fewest coins. Write the numbers of coins.

How much did each child spend? How much does each child have now?

LOW PRICE STORE

Snacks

Chips 28¢   CHOC 46¢   18¢

Drinks

JUICE 37¢   POP 25¢   5¢

I had 55¢. I bought (Chips) and (POP).

I had 60¢. I bought (CHOC) and (glass).

I had 60¢. I bought (snack) and (JUICE).

31)
```
  2 8 ¢
+ 2 5 ¢
------
      ¢
```
has ☐ ¢ left.

32)
```
    ☐☐ ¢
+   ☐☐ ¢
------
    ☐☐ ¢
```
has ☐ ¢ left.

33)
```
    ☐☐ ¢
+   ☐☐ ¢
------
    ☐☐ ¢
```
has ☐ ¢ left.

ACTIVITY

Jill and Mark share the coins equally. How many coins does each get? How much does each get?

1. Each has ☐ coins.

2. Each has ☐ ¢.

Shapes

Look at the shapes. Then tick ✔ the right sentences.

① [shape: rectangle]
A ☐ It has 3 sides.
B ☐ It has 4 sides.

② [shape: circle]
A ☐ It has 1 right angle.
B ☐ It has no angle.

Equal sides · Right angle · Equal sides

③ [shape: square]
A ☐ It has 4 equal sides.
B ☐ It has 3 right angles.

④ [shape: hexagon]
A ☐ It has 6 right angles.
B ☐ It has 6 sides.

⑤ [shape: triangle]
A ☐ It has 3 sides.
B ☐ It has 3 right angles.

Count and write the number of shapes.

⑥ Rectangle ☐

⑦ Triangle ☐

⑧ Circle ☐

⑨ Square ☐

⑩ Hexagon ☐

Two sides of my face match exactly. They have symmetry.

A shape having symmetry means it has both sides matching exactly.

Do these shapes have symmetry? Circle Yes or No.

  Yes No

  Yes No

  Yes No

  Yes No

  Yes No

  Yes No

Draw a line to cut each shape into two matching parts.

Symmetric

Draw the matching parts of each shape from the dotted line. Write their names in the ☐ .

㉔

㉕

The shapes you have learned are: rectangle, square, circle, triangle and hexagon.

㉖

㉗

Draw a line to cut each shape in half and colour half of it.

㉘   ㉙   ㉚   ㉛

Jill has made a shape with a tangram. Write the numbers in the **.**

This is a tangram.

A kitten

㉜

ACTIVITY

1. How many triangles are there ?

   ☐ triangles.

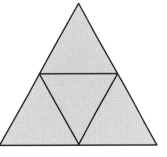

2. On each shape, draw as many lines as you can to cut the shape into matching parts.

   a.

   b.

3. Tick ✔ the shape formed with a tangram.

   a.

   ☐

   b.

   ☐

Pictographs

Count the pets and write the numbers.

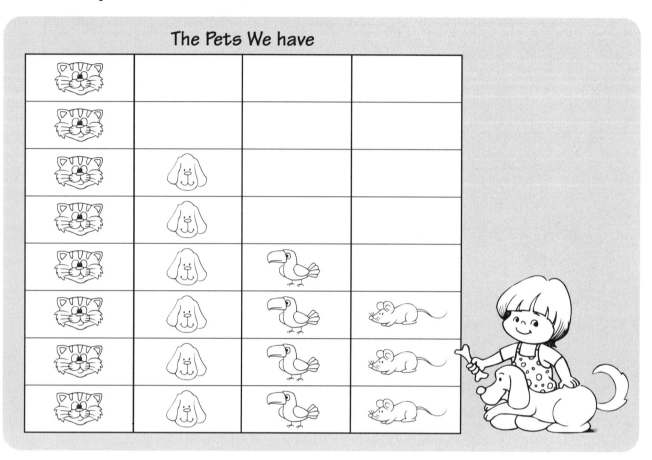

① There are ⬜ 🐱 .

② There are ⬜ 🐶 .

③ There are ⬜ 🐦 .

④ There are ⬜ 🐭 .

⑤ There are ⬜ more 🐱 than 🐶 .

⑥ There are ⬜ more 🐶 than 🐭 .

⑦ There are ⬜ pets in all.

Look at the pictograph and circle the right answers.

Here are the favourite foods of my class.

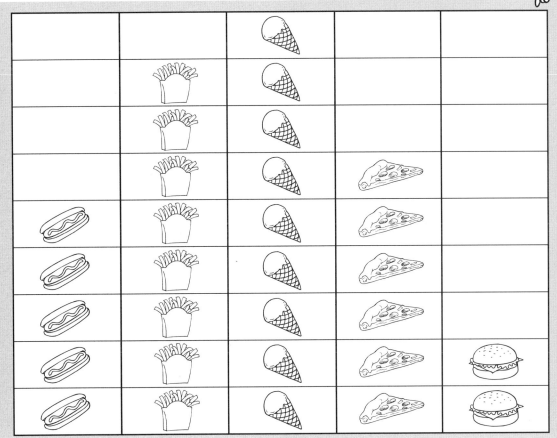

⑧ How many students like ?   5   7   9

⑨ 8 students like

⑩ Most students like

⑪ Fewest students like

⑫ How many students like and ?   15   16   17

⑬ How many students are there?   25   30   35

Read what Jill says. Make a graph and fill in the blanks.

I have 5 🧸 , 3 🚗 , 6 🐕 and 5 ⚪ .

⑭ Colour the ☐ to complete the graph.

Jill's Toys

⑮ There is ☐ more 🐕 than 🧸 .

⑯ There are ☐ more 🧸 than 🚗 .

⑰ There are ☐ 🧸 and ⚪ in all.

⑱ There are ☐ 🐕 and ⚪ in all.

⑲ There are ☐ toys in all.

Sort Jill's cards and circle the right answers.

⑳ Colour the ☐ to complete the graph.

Jill's Cards

㉑ How many ♡ are there?   5   6   7

㉒ How many ✿ are there?   5   6   7

㉓ Jill has the most   ♡   ☆   ✿

㉔ She has   15   16   17   cards in all.

A C T I V I T Y

Answer the questions.

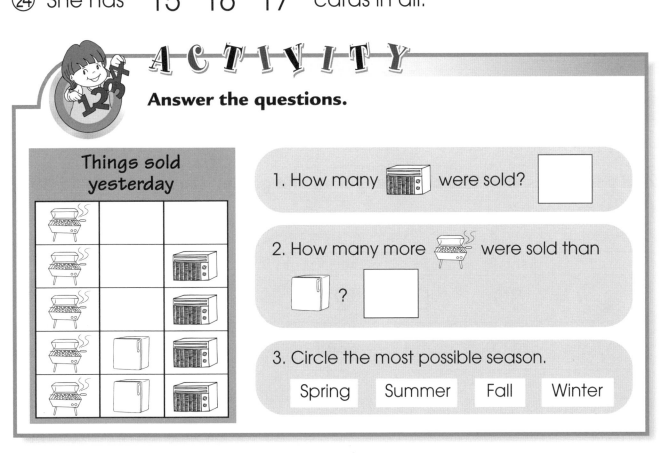

Things sold yesterday

1. How many [air conditioner] were sold?   ☐

2. How many more [grill] were sold than
   [refrigerator] ?   ☐

3. Circle the most possible season.

   Spring   Summer   Fall   Winter

Final Test

Write the numbers. (28 marks)

①
$$\begin{array}{r} 4\ 8 \\ +\ 3\ 9 \\ \hline \end{array}$$

②
$$\begin{array}{r} 5\ 2 \\ -\ 1\ 1 \\ \hline \end{array}$$

③
$$\begin{array}{r} \ 4 \\ +\ 3\ 7 \\ \hline \end{array}$$

④
$$\begin{array}{r} 4\ 6 \\ +\ 3\ 6 \\ \hline \end{array}$$

⑤
$$\begin{array}{r} 8\ 8 \\ -\ 5\ 5 \\ \hline \end{array}$$

⑥
$$\begin{array}{r} 9\ 3 \\ -\ 3\ 3 \\ \hline \end{array}$$

⑦ $25 + 16 = \boxed{}$

⑧ $3 + 19 = \boxed{}$

⑨ $23 + 57 = \boxed{}$

⑩ $48 - 17 = \boxed{}$

⑪ $62 - 62 = \boxed{}$

⑫ $79 - 59 = \boxed{}$

⑬ $14 + 23 + 11 = \boxed{}$

⑭ $59 + 11 + 6 = \boxed{}$

Read the points that the children got in the game. Do questions 15-19. (10 marks)

	1st ball	2nd ball	3rd ball
😊	39	0	25
😊	16	20	40
😊	43	28	0

⑮ How many points did get?

☐ + ☐ + ☐ = ☐

 got ☐ points.

⑯ How many points did get?

☐ + ☐ + ☐ = ☐

 got ☐ points.

⑰ How many points did get?

☐ + ☐ + ☐ = ☐

 got ☐ points.

⑱ How many more points did get than ?

☐ – ☐ = ☐

 got ☐ points more than .

⑲ Circle the child with the highest points.

Match the words to the pictures. (8 marks)

Use a ruler to measure the box. Write the numbers. (4 marks)

㉔ Length = ☐ cm

㉕ Width = ☐ cm

㉖ Height = ☐ cm

㉗ How many ▩ on the lid? ☐

Write the times or draw the clock hands. (10 marks)

Write the days and months. (5 marks)

㉝ Sunday → _____ → _____ →

   Wednesday → _____ → Friday → Saturday

㉞ May → _____ → _____ → August

Match the seasons to the temperatures. Tick ✔ the right ☐ . (4 marks)

Weather / Season	Warmest	Coldest	Getting warmer	Getting colder
㉟ Spring				
㊱ Summer				
㊲ Fall				
㊳ Winter				

Final Test

Write how much money each child has and tell who has more money.
(6 marks)

39 I have ☐ ¢ .

40 I have ☐ ¢ .

41 Circle the child that has more money.

Pay with the fewest coins. Write the numbers. (4 marks)

42 🚗 35¢				
43 🔝 40¢				
44 🌸🌸 26¢				
45 🔫 48¢				

Draw a line to cut each shape into two matching parts. (3 marks)

㊻

㊼

㊽

Draw the matching parts of each shape from the dotted line. (4 marks)

㊾

㊿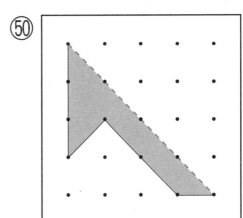

Show how many 🍬 the children got in the game. (6 marks)

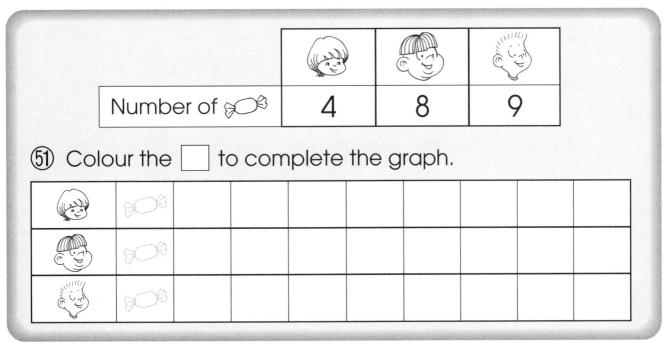

Number of 🍬	4	8	9

51) Colour the ☐ to complete the graph.

Look at Jill's pictograph and answer the questions. (8 marks)

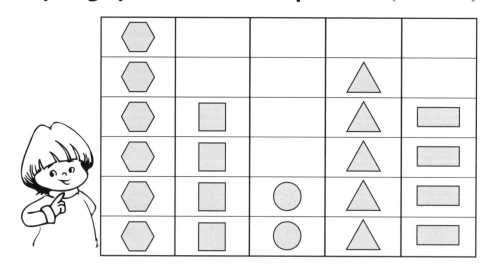

㊾ Write the numbers.

   a. Jill has ☐ hexagons.

   b. Jill has ☐ squares.

   c. Jill has ☐ more triangles than circles.

   d. Jill has ☐ hexagons and circles in all.

㊾ Circle the right answers.

   a. Jill has the most | hexagons | triangles | rectangles | .

   b. Jill has the fewest | rectangles | squares | circles | .

   c. Jill has the same number of | squares |

   | hexagons | and | triangles | rectangles | .

SCORE

100

Section IV

Overview

In Section III, children were introduced to the five major areas of mathematics: Number Sense and Numeration, Measurement, Geometry and Spatial Sense, Patterning and Algebra, and Data Management and Probability.

In this section, concepts of shape, money, measurement, graph, addition and subtraction are further developed and practised in integrated exercises.

Solving "story problems" provides children with practice in reading as well as translating words into mathematical terms. The exercises describe everyday situations to provide context and interest for the Grade 1 students.

Use the pictures to answer the questions.

① How many 🍎 are there in Helen's basket? _____ 🍎

② How many 🍎 are there in Barry's basket? _____ 🍎

③ Who has more 🍎 ? _____

④ How many ⬚ are there in Dan's tower? _____ ⬚

⑤ How many ⬚ are there in Rick's tower? _____ ⬚

⑥ How many ⬚ are there in Eva's tower? _____ ⬚

⑦ Who has the most ⬚ ? _____

⑧ Who has the fewest ⬚ ? _____

⑨ If Eva puts 1 more ⬚ on her tower, how many ⬚ are there in her new tower?

_____ ⬚

Jamie's cookies	Carmen's cookies	Lucy's cookies

⑩ How many 🍪 does Jamie have? _____ 🍪

⑪ How many 🍪 does Carmen have? _____ 🍪

⑫ How many 🍪 does Lucy have? _____ 🍪

⑬ How many 🍪 could Jamie give to his friends if he ate one himself? _____ 🍪

⑭ How many 🍪 would Lucy have if she got one from Jamie? _____ 🍪

Fill in the blanks.

⑮ How many boys are there? _____ boys

⑯ How many girls are there? _____ girls

⑰ How many children are there? _____ children

⑱ Who is the 1st on the line? _____

⑲ Who is the 3rd on the line? _____

Addition and Subtraction to 10

See how many stickers each child has. Answer the questions.

Ann	Bobby	Carol	Deb

① Ann has _____ ☺ .

② Bobby has _____ ☺ .

③ Carol has _____ ☺ .

④ Deb has _____ ☺ .

⑤ _____ has the most ☺ ; _____ has the fewest ☺ .

⑥ Ann and Bobby have _____ ☺ in all.

⑦ Bobby and Deb have _____ ☺ in all.

⑧ Ann and Deb have _____ ☺ in all.

⑨ Ann has _____ fewer ☺ than Carol.

⑩ Carol has _____ more ☺ than Bobby.

⑪ Carol has _____ more ☺ than Deb.

Use the pictures to answer the questions.

⑫ How many do Kim and Betty have? _____

⑬ How many more does Kim have than Betty? _____

⑭ Kim gives 1 to Betty, how many does he have now? _____

⑮ How many does Betty have now? _____

⑯ How many are there in all? _____

⑰ How many more are there on the plate than in the box? _____

⑱ There are 4 chocolate on the plate. How many on the plate are not chocolate flavour? _____

⑲ Joey puts 3 more on the plate. How many are on the plate now? _____

⑳ Julia takes 2 from the box. How many are left? _____

See how many biscuits each child ate yesterday. Then answer the questions.

	Brian	Dave	Beth
Morning	🍪🍪	🍪🍪🍪	🍪🍪🍪 🍪🍪
Afternoon	🍪🍪🍪🍪	🍪🍪🍪🍪 🍪🍪🍪	🍪🍪

㉑ How many 🍪 did Brian eat in all? _____ 🍪

㉒ How many 🍪 did Dave eat in all? _____ 🍪

㉓ How many 🍪 did Beth eat in all? _____ 🍪

㉔ How many 🍪 did the children eat in the morning? _____ 🍪

㉕ How many more 🍪 did Brian eat in the afternoon than in the morning? _____ 🍪

㉖ How many fewer 🍪 did Dave eat in the morning than in the afternoon? _____ 🍪

㉗ How many fewer 🍪 did Beth eat in the afternoon than in the morning? _____ 🍪

㉘ If Beth ate 3 more 🍪 in the afternoon, how many 🍪 did he eat the whole day? _____ 🍪

See what Jack has for his birthday party. Then write the numbers.

㉙ 3 ◯ are red; _____ ◯ are not red.

㉚ If 2 ◯ burst, _____ ◯ are left.

㉛ Jack's mom buys 6 ⬭ . _____ ⬭ are not on the table.

㉜ Jack fills 3 ▢ with pop. _____ ▢ are not filled.

㉝ Jack is 7 years old. He needs to put _____ more 🕯 on the cake.

㉞ 4 boys and 3 girls come to the party. _____ children come to the party in all.

㉟ Each guest takes 1 ◿ . _____ ◿ are left.

㊱ Each girl takes 1 🍴 . _____ 🍴 are left.

㊲ There are 10 ⬭ on the table. If each girl takes 1 ⬭ , _____ ⬭ are left.

See how many candies each child collected at Halloween. Count and write the numbers. Then answer the questions.

⑤ ate 5 🍬 . How many 🍬 are left? _____ 🍬

⑥ ate 3 🍬 . How many 🍬 are left? _____ 🍬

⑦ gave 2 🍬 to 👧 . How many 🍬

are left? _____ 🍬

⑧ How many 🍬 does 👧 have now? _____ 🍬

Look at the fruits Brad's mom bought. Count and write the numbers. Then answer the questions.

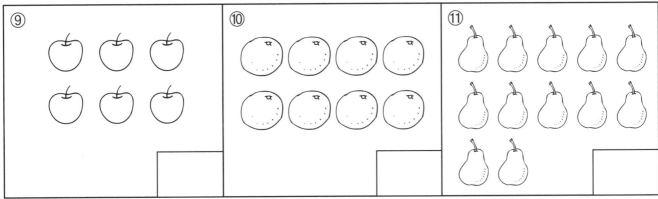

⑫	How many 🍎 and 🍊 did Brad's mom buy in all? _____ 🍎 🍊 in all	$\begin{array}{r} 6 \\ + 8 \\ \hline \end{array}$
⑬	How many 🍊 and 🍐 did Brad's mom buy in all? _____ 🍊 🍐 in all	
⑭	How many more 🍐 are there than 🍎 ? _____ more 🍐	
⑮	How many more 🍐 are there than 🍊 ? _____ more 🍐	
⑯	Brad's mom gives 5 🍐 to a friend. How many 🍐 are left? _____ 🍐 left	

Answer the questions.

⑰ Ann has 7 🌼 ; Grace has 11 🌼 . How many 🌼 do they have in all?

$$\underline{\qquad 7 + 11 \qquad} = \underline{\qquad}$$ $$\underline{\qquad}$$ 🌼 in all

⑱ How many more 🌼 does Grace have than Ann?

$$\underline{\qquad\qquad\qquad} = \underline{\qquad}$$ $$\underline{\qquad}$$ more 🌼

⑲ In Mrs Ling's class, there are 17 👦👧 . 5 are 👧 . How many 👦 are there?

$$\underline{\qquad\qquad\qquad} = \underline{\qquad}$$ $$\underline{\qquad}$$ 👦

⑳ How many more 👦 are there than 👧 ?

$$\underline{\qquad\qquad\qquad} = \underline{\qquad}$$ $$\underline{\qquad}$$ more 👦

㉑ Tim has 13 🍫 ; Rick has 7 🍫 . How many 🍫 do they have in all?

$$\underline{\qquad\qquad\qquad} = \underline{\qquad}$$ $$\underline{\qquad}$$ 🍫 in all

㉒ How many more 🍫 does Tim have than Rick?

$$\underline{\qquad\qquad\qquad} = \underline{\qquad}$$ $$\underline{\qquad}$$ more 🍫

㉓ Mrs White buys 3 (donut). Mrs Wenn buys 11 (donut). How many (donut) do they buy in all?

_____ = _____   _____ (donut) in all

㉔ How many more (donut) does Mrs Wenn buy than Mrs White?

_____ = _____   _____ more (donut)

㉕ Mr Stanley has 3 (bag) of (apple). Each (bag) has 6 (apple). How many (apple) are there in all?

_____ = _____   _____ (apple) in all

㉖ If Mr Stanley wants to have 20 (apple), how many more (apple) does he need to buy?

_____ = _____   _____ more (apple)

㉗ Ben is 12 years old. How old was he 4 years ago?

_____ = _____   _____ years old

㉘ How old will he be after 5 years?

_____ = _____   _____ years old

UNIT 4 Shapes

Write 'cone', 'cylinder', 'prism' or 'sphere' in the boxes. Then match similar shapes.

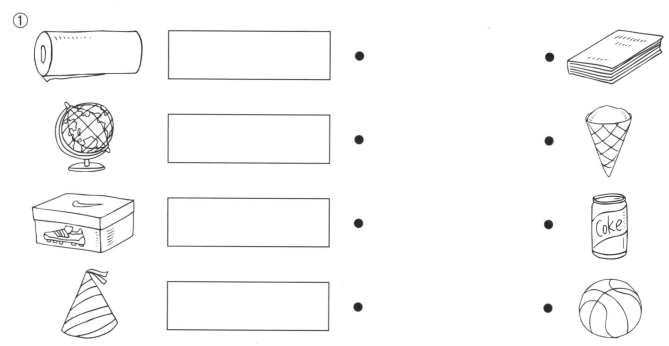

①

Mandy gets 4 boxes of chocolates for Valentine's Day. Write 'cube', 'cylinder', 'prism' or 'pyramid' in the boxes. Then put a check mark ✔ in the circle for the one that can roll.

②   ③

④   ⑤

Check ✔ the correct sentences and cross out ✗ the wrong ones.

⑥ A prism can slide. ◯

⑦ A cylinder can slide and roll. ◯

⑧ A sphere can roll but not slide. ◯

⑨ A cube can roll and slide. ◯

⑩ A pyramid can roll. ◯

See how many blocks are needed to build each tower. Then answer the questions.

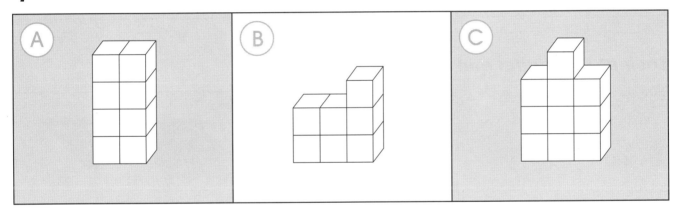

⑪ How many blocks are needed to build tower A? _____ blocks

⑫ How many blocks are needed to build tower B? _____ blocks

⑬ How many blocks are needed to build tower C? _____ blocks

⑭ Which of the towers is a prism? Tower _____

⑮ What is the fewest number of blocks you need to
   add on tower B to make it a prism? _____

Look at the shaded part of each flag. Then name the shape.

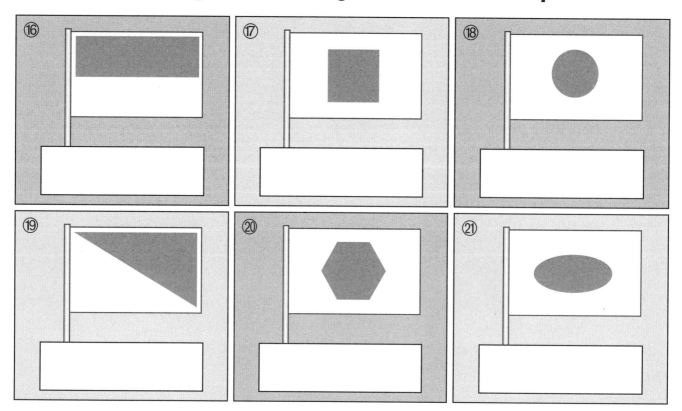

Look at the shapes and complete the table.

	㉒	㉓	㉔	㉕
Number of sides				
Number of corners				

Draw a line to cut each shape into two matching parts.

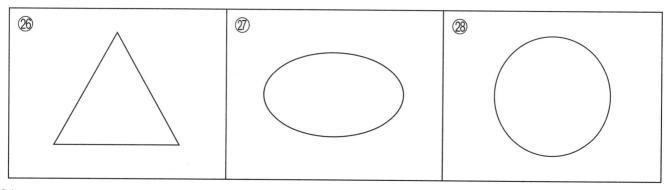

Draw the matching part of each shape from the dotted line.

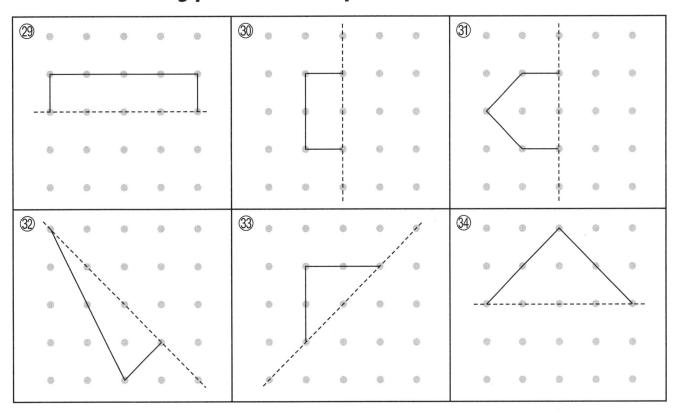

See how many books Uncle Bill uses to cover each board. Estimate and count. Write the numbers.

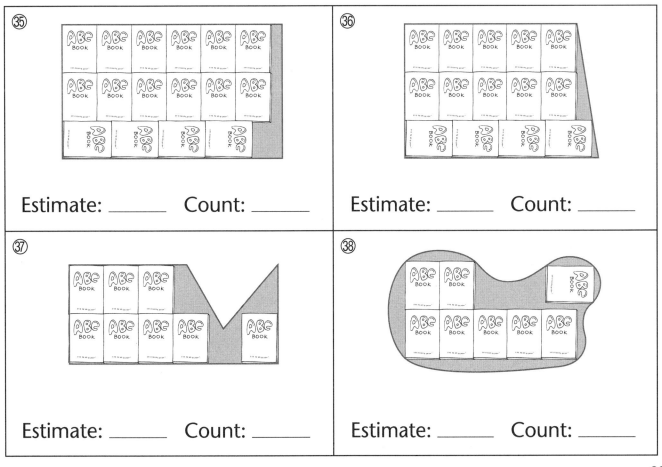

35 Estimate: _____ Count: _____

36 Estimate: _____ Count: _____

37 Estimate: _____ Count: _____

38 Estimate: _____ Count: _____

Solid Column Graphs

The graph shows which sports the students like best. Check ✔ the correct answers.

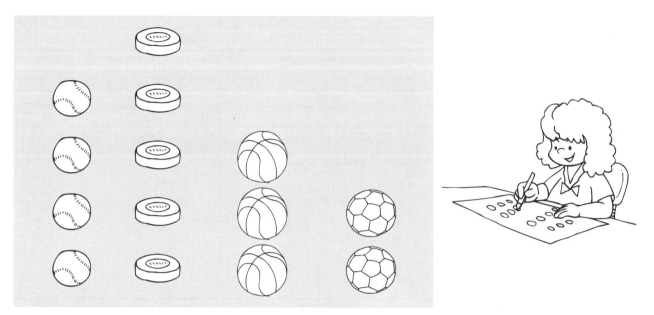

① Which is the most popular sport?

   Ⓐ   Ⓑ   Ⓒ

② Which is the least popular sport?

   Ⓐ   Ⓑ   Ⓒ

③ How many students like best?

   Ⓐ 3   Ⓑ 4   Ⓒ 5

④ How many more students like than ?

   Ⓐ 1   Ⓑ 2   Ⓒ 3

⑤ How many students are asked?

   Ⓐ 12   Ⓑ 13   Ⓒ 14

Kay, Kim and Karen are collecting stickers. See how many stickers they have and answer the questions.

⑥ Who has the most ⭐ ? _____

⑦ Who has the fewest ⭐ ? _____

⑧ How many ⭐ does Kay have? _____ ⭐

⑨ How many ⭐ does Kim have? _____ ⭐

⑩ How many ⭐ does Karen have? _____ ⭐

⑪ How many ⭐ do Kay and Kim have? _____ ⭐

⑫ How many more ⭐ does Karen have than Kim? _____ ⭐

⑬ How many ⭐ do they have in all? _____ ⭐

⑭ If Kay collects 5 more ⭐ , how many does he have in all? _____ ⭐

Count the fish in the tank. Then answer the questions and colour the pictures to complete the graph.

⑮ How many 🐟 are there? _____ 🐟

⑯ How many 🐠 are there? _____ 🐠

⑰ How many 🐡 are there? _____ 🐡

⑱ How many 🐟 are there? _____ 🐟

⑲

Fish in the Tank

Count the animals in the pet shop. Then answer the questions and colour the pictures to complete the graph.

20 How many types of animals are there?   _____ types

21 How many are there?   _____

22 How many are there?   _____

23 How many are there?   _____

24 How many are there?   _____

25

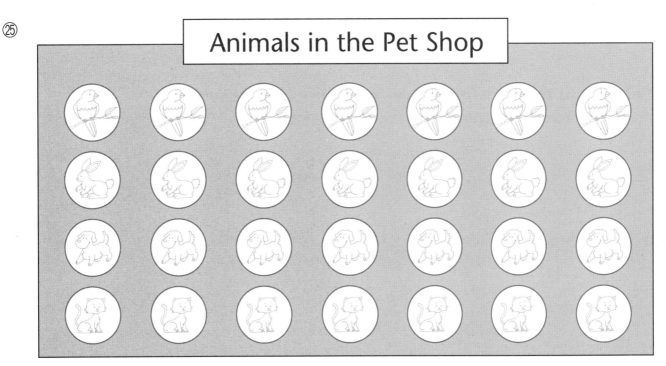

Animals in the Pet Shop

Count the ice cubes each child has. Then answer the questions.

① How many 🧊 does Greg have?   _____ 🧊

② How many 🧊 does Pat have?   _____ 🧊

③ How many 🧊 does Sam have?   _____ 🧊

④ How many more 🧊 does Grey have than Sam?   _____ 🧊

⑤ If Greg gives Pat 2 🧊, how many 🧊 does Pat have in all?   _____ 🧊

⑥ If 3 of Sam's 🧊 melted, how many 🧊 would be left?   _____ 🧊

Colour the things which have the shape of a sphere.

⑦

The pictures show how many glasses of milk the children drink in a week. Use the pictures to answer the questions.

Sue	Mabel	Paul	Sam

⑧ Sue drinks _____ in a week.

⑨ Mabel drinks _____ in a week.

⑩ Paul drinks _____ in a week.

⑪ Sam drinks _____ 🥛 in a week.

⑫ Sue and Paul drink _____ 🥛 in all.

⑬ Mabel and Sam drink _____ 🥛 in all.

⑭ Mabel drinks _____ more 🥛 than Paul.

⑮ The girls drink _____ 🥛 in all.

⑯ The boys drink _____ 🥛 in all.

⑰ The boys drink _____ 🥛 fewer than the girls.

⑱ If Paul drinks 7 more 🥛 , he would drink _____ 🥛 in a week.

Look at the shapes of Judy's containers. Check ✔ the correct answers and colour the pictures to complete the graph.

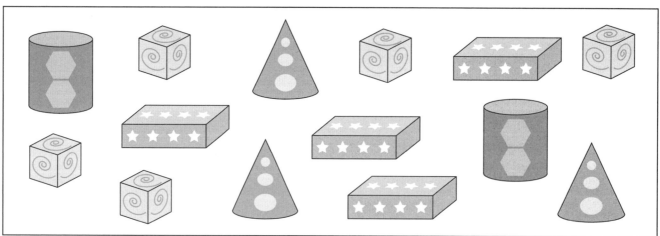

⑲ How many types of shapes are in Judy's collection?

Ⓐ 2   Ⓑ 3   Ⓒ 4

⑳ Which shape does Judy have the most?

Ⓐ cylinder   Ⓑ cube   Ⓒ prism

㉑ How many cones does Judy have?

Ⓐ 2   Ⓑ 3   Ⓒ 4

㉒ How many cubes and cylinders does Judy have in all?

Ⓐ 6   Ⓑ 7   Ⓒ 8

㉓ How many more cubes are there than cones?

Ⓐ 2   Ⓑ 3   Ⓒ 4

㉔ How many containers does Judy have in all?

Ⓐ 12   Ⓑ 13   Ⓒ 14

㉕

Judy's Collection

Lucy traces the shapes on the paper. Match the containers with the shapes and write the names of the shapes.

㉖

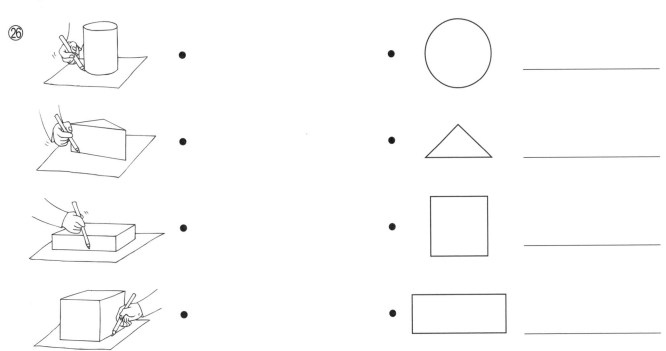

Draw a line to cut each shape into two matching parts.

㉗ ㉘ ㉙

UNIT 6 Numbers 20 to 100

Count and write how many crayons are in each group. Then answer the questions.

① 10 10 10

Group A: ____

② 10 10 10 10 10

Group B: ____

③ 10 10 10 10

Group C: ____

④ 10 10

Group D: ____

⑤ Which group has the most crayons?

Group _____

⑥ Which group has the fewest crayons?

Group _____

⑦ Put the groups in order from the one that has the most crayons to the one that has the fewest.

Group _____ , Group _____ , Group _____ , Group _____

⑧ If Wayne puts 10 more crayons in Group B, how many crayons are there in all?

_____ crayons

⑨ If George takes 10 crayons away form Group C, how many crayons will be left?

_____ crayons

⑩ Jill has 1 crayon more than Group D. How many crayons does she have?

_____ crayons

The children put the pennies in piles of 10. Write how many pennies each child has. Then answer the questions.

Lily has _____ .

Amy has _____ .

Ivan has _____ .

⑭ _____ has the most money.

⑮ _____ has the least money.

⑯ Put the children in order from the one who has the most money to the one who has the least.

_____ , _____ , _____

⑰ Ivan gives 1 pile of 🪙 to Lily. Ivan has _____ 🪙 left.

⑱ Amy gets 5 more 🪙 . She has _____ 🪙 in all.

See how many jelly beans each child has. Use the table to answer the questions.

	Brenda	Derek	Mike	Dan
Number of jelly beans	79	52	69	78

⑲ Who has seventy-eight jelly beans? _____

⑳ Who has 10 fewer jelly beans than Brenda? _____

㉑ Who has 1 more jelly bean than Dan? _____

㉒ Who has the most jelly beans? _____

㉓ Who has the fewest jelly beans? _____

㉔ Put the children in order from the one who has the fewest jelly beans to the one who has the most.

_____ , _____ , _____ , _____

㉕ Mike gives 1 jelly bean to Derek. Mike has _____ jelly beans left and Derek has _____ jelly beans in all.

㉖ Brenda gives 2 jelly beans to Dan. Dan has _____ jelly beans in all and Brenda has _____ jelly beans left.

㉗ _____ has the most jelly beans now.

Read what the children say. Then write the numbers on the fence.

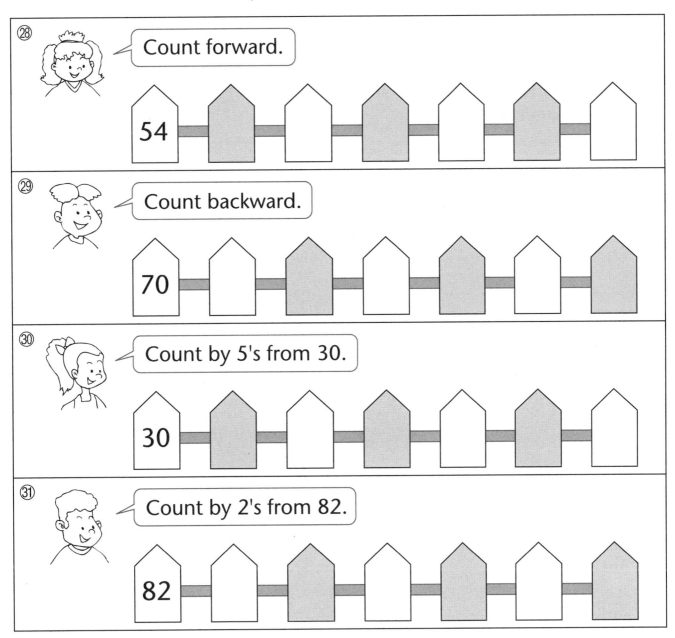

㉘ Count forward.

54

㉙ Count backward.

70

㉚ Count by 5's from 30.

30

㉛ Count by 2's from 82.

82

Answer the questions.

㉜ Jim has 68 ⊙ ; May has ⊙ . Who has more ⊙ ? _____

㉝ William has 48 🍭 ; Stephen has 51 🍭 . Who has fewer 🍭 ? _____

㉞ Alvin has 25 🍬 ; Louis has 20 more 🍬 than Alvin. How many 🍬 does Louis have? _____ 🍬

Calculators may be used to calculate or check answers. Count and write how many boys and girls are in each group. Then use the pictures to answer the questions.

① Group A		② Group B	

③ How many boys are there in all?

_____ = _____   _____ boys

④ How many girls are there in all?

_____ = _____   _____ girls

⑤ How many children are in Group A?

_____ = _____   _____ children

⑥ How many children are in Group B?

_____ = _____   _____ children

⑦ How many children are there in all?

_____ = _____   _____ children

See how many pins are in each pincushion. Use the pictures to answer the questions.

⑧ How many 🖈 are in the small pincushion? _____ 🖈

⑨ How many 🖈 are in the big pincushion? _____ 🖈

⑩ How many 🖈 are there in all?

_____ = _____   _____ 🖈

⑪ How many more 🖈 are in the big pincushion than in the small one?

_____ = _____   _____ 🖈

⑫ If Mrs Smith puts 15 more 🖈 in the small pincushion, how many 🖈 are there in the small pincushion?

_____ = _____   _____ 🖈

⑬ If Aunt Molly puts 15 more 🖈 in the big pincushion, how many 🖈 are there in the big pincushion?

_____ = _____   _____ 🖈

⑭ If Lucy takes out 16 🖈 from the big pincushion, how many 🖈 are left in the big pincushion?

_____ = _____   _____ 🖈

Brenda, Mike and Dan collected some shells on Monday and Tuesday. Look at the record and answer the questions.

	Monday	Tuesday
Brenda	15	17
Mike	11	14
Dan	18	19

⑮ How many 🐚 did Brenda collect in all?

_____ = _____   _____ 🐚

⑯ How many 🐚 did Mike collect in all?

_____ = _____   _____ 🐚

⑰ How many 🐚 did Dan collect in all?

_____ = _____   _____ 🐚

⑱ How many more 🐚 did Dan collect than Mike?

_____ = _____   _____ 🐚

⑲ How many 🐚 did the children collect on Monday?

_____ = _____   _____ 🐚

⑳ How many 🐚 did the children collect on Tuesday?

_____ = _____   _____ 🐚

Look at the record showing the loaves of bread baked and sold in the past 3 days. Then answer the questions.

	Thursday	Friday	Saturday
Number of 🍞 baked	21	24	28
Number of 🍞 sold	17	18	19

㉑ How many 🍞 were left on Thursday?

_____ = _____   _____ 🍞

㉒ How many 🍞 were left on Friday?

_____ = _____   _____ 🍞

㉓ How many 🍞 were left on Saturday?

_____ = _____   _____ 🍞

㉔ How many 🍞 did the baker bake on Thursday and Friday?

_____ = _____   _____ 🍞

㉕ How many 🍞 did the baker bake on Thursday and Saturday?

_____ = _____   _____ 🍞

㉖ How many 🍞 were sold on Friday and Saturday?

_____ = _____   _____ 🍞

Addition and Subtraction to 100

Calculators can be used to calculate or check answers. Count and write how many shells each child collected. Then answer the questions.

① Peter

② Roger

③ Tina

④ How many 🐚 did Peter and Tina collect in all?

[ ] + [ ] = [ ]

They collected [ ] 🐚 in all.

[ ]
+ [ ]
―――
[ ]

⑤ How many more 🐚 did Tina collect than Roger?

[ ] − [ ] = [ ]

Tina collected [ ] more 🐚 than Roger.

[ ]
− [ ]
―――
[ ]

⑥ How many 🐚 did the boys collect in all?

□ + □ = □

They collected □ 🐚 in all.

\+ □
□
□

⑦ How many more 🐚 did Peter collect than Tina?

□ – □ = □

Peter collected □ more 🐚 than Tina.

– □
□
□

⑧ Tina's goal was to collect 60 🐚. How many more 🐚 must she collect to meet her goal?

□ – □ = □

She must collect □ more 🐚.

– □
□
□

⑨ Peter's goal was to collect 35 🐚. How many more 🐚 had he collected ?

□ – □ = □

He had collected □ more 🐚.

– □
□
□

⑩ How many 🐚 did the children collect in all?

□ + □ + □ = □

They collected □ 🐚 in all.

\+ □
□
□
□

See how many animals are on each farm. Then use the table to answer the questions.

	Fred's Farm	Roy's Farm	Andy's Farm
(chicken)	37	29	27
(cow)	16	28	23
(horse)	15	16	49

⑪ Whose farm has the most (chicken)?　　　　　　　　＿＿＿＿＿＿＿'s farm

⑫ Whose farm has the most (cow)?　　　　　　　　　＿＿＿＿＿＿＿'s farm

⑬ Whose farm has the fewest (horse)?　　　　　　　　＿＿＿＿＿＿＿'s farm

⑭ How many animals are there on Fred's farm?

＿＿＿＿＿＿＿＿＿＿＿＿＿＿ = ＿＿＿＿＿＿＿　　　＿＿＿＿＿ animals

⑮ How many animals are there on Roy's farm?

＿＿＿＿＿＿＿＿＿＿＿＿＿＿ = ＿＿＿＿＿＿＿　　　＿＿＿＿＿ animals

⑯ How many animals are there on Andy's farm?

＿＿＿＿＿＿＿＿＿＿＿＿＿＿ = ＿＿＿＿＿＿＿　　　＿＿＿＿＿ animals

⑰ How many (chicken) are on these three farms?

＿＿＿＿＿＿＿＿＿＿＿＿＿＿ = ＿＿＿＿＿＿＿　　　＿＿＿＿＿ (chicken)

⑱ How many 🐮 are on these three farms?

_____ = _____   _____ 🐮

⑲ How many 🐴 are on these three farms?

_____ = _____   _____ 🐴

⑳ How many 4-legged animals are on Fred's farm?

_____ = _____   _____ animals

㉑ If Fred gives 12 🐔 to Roy, how many 🐔 are left?

_____ = _____   _____ 🐔

㉒ If Roy gets 12 🐔 from Fred, how many 🐔 does he have in all?

_____ = _____   _____ 🐔

㉓ If Andy buys 18 more 🐮 , how many 🐮 does he have in all?

_____ = _____   _____ 🐮

㉔ On Andy's farm, there are 16 white 🐴 . How many 🐴 on Andy's farm are not white?

_____ = _____   _____ 🐴

㉕ On Andy's farm, there are 13 cocks. How many hens are there?

_____ = _____   _____ hens

UNIT **9** **Money**

Write how much each item costs. Then answer the questions.

①	CHOCOLATE BAR — 25¢, 10¢, 5¢, 1¢, 1¢	☐ ¢
②	Juicy GUM — 10¢, 10¢, 1¢, 1¢, 1¢	☐ ¢
③	Chips — 25¢, 5¢, 1¢	☐ ¢
④	Candy Ring — 25¢, 10¢, 1¢, 1¢, 1¢, 1¢	☐ ¢

⑤ How many items cost more than 30¢? _____ items

⑥ Which is the most expensive item? _____

⑦ Which is the cheapest item? _____

⑧	Kathy buys 1 CHOCOLATE BAR and 1 Juicy GUM. How much does she pay in all? She pays _____ ¢ in all.	42 + 23 ------
⑨	Lucy buys 1 Chips and 1 Candy Ring. How much does she pay in all? She pays _____ ¢ in all.	

⑩ Sean buys 1 Chips . How much change does he get from 50¢?

He gets _____ ¢ change.

⑪ Kim buys 1 Candy Ring . Sandy buys 1 Juicy Gum .

How much more does Kim pay?

Kim pays _____ ¢ more.

⑫ Jack buys 2 CHOCOLATE BAR . How much does he pay in all?

He pays _____ ¢ in all.

⑬ The Chips is on sale. It costs 7¢ less. How much does it cost now?

It costs _____ ¢ now.

⑭ Cliff has 18¢. He wants to buy 1 Juicy Gum .

How much more money does he need?

He needs _____ ¢ more.

⑮ Amy has 24¢ and Brian has 18¢. They want to buy 1 item together. Which item with the highest price can they buy?

They can buy _____ .

See how much each toy costs. Then complete the tables and answer the questions.

⑯

Number of 🪀	1	2	3
Cost	27 ¢	¢	¢

⑰

Number of 🎺	1	2	3
Cost			

⑱

Number of	1	2	3
Cost			

⑲ Jane buys a 🪀 and a 🎺 . How much does she pay in all?

_____ = _____ _____ ¢ in all

⑳ Alexander buys a 🎺 and a . How much does he pay in all?

_____ = _____ _____ ¢ in all

㉑ Raymond pays 50¢ for a 🪀 . How much change does he get?

_____ = _____ _____ ¢ change

Look at the toys on the previous page. Then answer the questions and check ✔ the fewest coins to match the answers.

㉒ Janet pays 50¢ for a 🌀 . How much change does she get?

_____ = _____   _____ ¢ change

㉓

㉔ Eddie pays 35¢ for a 🪀 . How much change does he get?

_____ = _____   _____ ¢ change

㉕ (coins)

㉖ Tim buys 1 🪀 and 2 🌀 . How much does he pay in all?

_____ = _____   _____ ¢ in all

㉗ (coins)

㉘ Gary buys 1 🌀 and 2 🌀 . How much does he pay in all?

_____ = _____   _____ ¢ in all

㉙

See how long each pencil is. Then fill in the blanks.

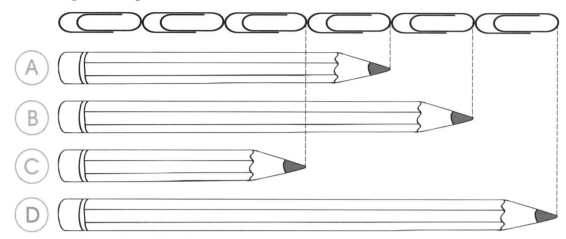

① Pencil A has the same length as _____ ⬭ .

② Pencil B has the same length as _____ ⬭ .

③ Pencil C has the same length as _____ ⬭ .

④ Pencil D has the same length as _____ ⬭ .

⑤ Put the pencils in order from the longest to the shortest.

_____ , _____ , _____ , _____

See how heavy each toy is. Then fill in the blanks.

⑥ 🚌 has the same weight as _____ 🚗 .

⑦ 🤖 has the same weight as _____ 🚌 .

⑧ Put the toys in order from the lightest to the heaviest.

_____ , _____ , _____

Write the time or draw the clock hands to show the times. Then answer the questions.

Mr Smith's Meal Times

⑨ Breakfast — Half-past seven

⑩ Lunch —

⑪ Supper — Seven o'clock

⑫ Does Mr Smith eat breakfast before or after seven o'clock? _____

⑬ Mr Smith comes home at half-past six. Is he early or late for supper? _____

Count and write the numbers.

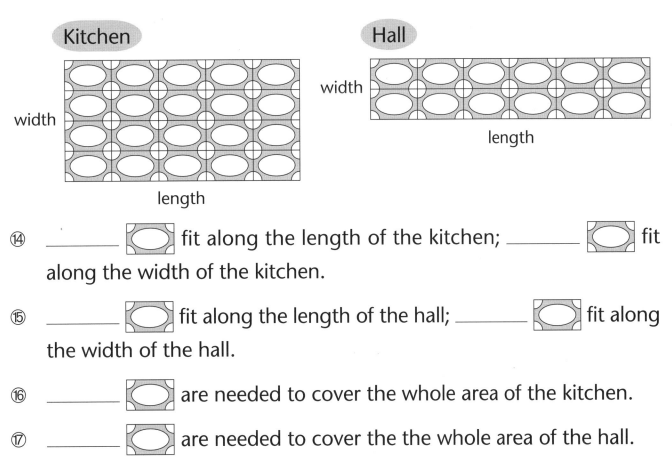

Kitchen

width

length

Hall

width

length

⑭ _____ ⬭ fit along the length of the kitchen; _____ ⬭ fit along the width of the kitchen.

⑮ _____ ⬭ fit along the length of the hall; _____ ⬭ fit along the width of the hall.

⑯ _____ ⬭ are needed to cover the whole area of the kitchen.

⑰ _____ ⬭ are needed to cover the the whole area of the hall.

UNIT 11 Pictographs

The children played their favourite sports last weekend. Look at the pictograph and check ✔ the correct answers.

Sports Played Last Weekend

① Which sport did the most children play?

   Ⓐ   Ⓑ   Ⓒ

② Which sport did the fewest children play?

   Ⓐ   Ⓑ   Ⓒ

③ How many children played   ?

   Ⓐ 3   Ⓑ 4   Ⓒ 5

④ How many children played   ?

   Ⓐ 3   Ⓑ 4   Ⓒ 5

⑤ How many children played   or   ?

   Ⓐ 7   Ⓑ 8   Ⓒ 9

⑥ How many more children played   than   ?

   Ⓐ 3   Ⓑ 2   Ⓒ 1

⑦ Which is the most possible season?

   Ⓐ Spring   Ⓑ Summer   Ⓒ Fall   Ⓓ Winter

Read the pictograph and answer the questions.

Number of Marbles Each Child Has

Joe	◉ ◉ ◉ ◉ ◉ ◉
Anita	◉ ◉
Britt	◉ ◉ ◉ ◉ ◉
Paula	◉ ◉ ◉ ◉ ◉ ◉ ◉ ◉

⑧ Who has the most marbles? _____

⑨ Who has the fewest marbles? _____

⑩ Who has more marbles than Anita but fewer than Joe? _____

⑪ How many ◉ do Joe and Britt have in all? _____ ◉

⑫ How many ◉ do Anita and Paula have in all? _____ ◉

⑬ How many more ◉ does Joe have than Anita? _____ ◉

⑭ How many more ◉ does Paula have than Britt? _____ ◉

⑮ How many children have 6 or more marbles? _____ children

⑯ How many ◉ do the children have in all? _____ ◉

⑰ If Paula gives Britt 1 ◉ , how many ◉ does Paula have now? _____ ◉

⑱ If Britt gets 1 more ◉ , does she have more ◉ than Joe? _____

Count how many toys Debbie has. Then colour the pictograph and circle the correct answers.

Debbie's Toys

⑲

Debbie's Toys

㉚ How many 🧸 does Debbie have? 6 7 8

㉑ How many ⚽ does Debbie have? 6 7 8

㉒ How many 🪆 and 🧸 does Debbie have? 12 13 14

㉓ How many 🪀 and ⚽ does Debbie have? 8 9 10

㉔ How many of Debbie's toys are not 🧸 ? 12 13 14

㉕ Which kind of toy does Debbie have the most? 🪆 🧸 🪀

㉖ Which kind of toy does Debbie have the fewest? 🪆 🪀 ⚽

㉗ How many more 🧸 than 🪆 does Debbie have? 3 4 5

㉘ How many toys does Debbie have in all? 19 20 21

㉙ On Debbie's birthday, she gets 4 more 🪆 . How many 🪆 does she have now? 7 8 9

Look at the pictures. Then check ✔ the correct answers.

① Is there a better chance that you will pick a 🌼 or a 🌷 ?

   A 🌼   B 🌷

② Is there a better chance that you will pick a 🐚 or a 🐚 ?

   A 🐚   B 🐚

③ Is there a better chance that you will pick a 😴 or a 😊 ?

   A 😴   B 😊

④ Is there a better chance that you will pick a ☯ or a ☯ ?

   A ☯   B ☯

⑤ Which temperature is more likely in February in Toronto?

   A   B

⑥ What time is more likely to have breakfast?

   A   B

Look at the bag of marbles. Then check ✔ the correct answers.

⑦ Which word is the best to describe the chance of picking a green marble?

Ⓐ likely　　Ⓑ unlikely　　Ⓒ never

⑧ Which word is the best to describe the chance of picking a red marble?

Ⓐ likely　　Ⓑ unlikely　　Ⓒ never

⑨ Which word is the best to describe the chance of picking a black marble?

Ⓐ likely　　Ⓑ unlikely　　Ⓒ never　　Ⓓ maybe

⑩ What colour are you most likely to pick from the bag?

Ⓐ yellow　　Ⓑ green　　Ⓒ red　　Ⓓ black

Look at the spinner. Then answer the questions.

⑪

a. Which word is the best to describe the chance of spinning a 🍟 ?

Ⓐ never　　Ⓑ unlikely　　Ⓒ likely

b. Which word is the best to describe the chance of spinning a 🍦 ?

Ⓐ never　　Ⓑ maybe　　Ⓒ likely

c. Which word is the best to describe the chance of spinning a 🍫 ?

Ⓐ never　　Ⓑ maybe　　Ⓒ unlikely

Count and write how much each child has. Then answer the questions.

① Billy

② Cam

③ How much do Billy and Cam have in all?

◻ + ◻ = ◻

They have ◻ ¢ in all.

◻
+ ◻
‾‾‾
◻

④ How much more does Billy have than Cam?

◻ – ◻ = ◻

Billy has ◻ ¢ more than Cam.

◻
– ◻
‾‾‾
◻

⑤ Uncle Tom gives Billy 5¢. How much does Tom have now?

◻ + ◻ = ◻

Tom has ◻ ¢ now.

◻
+ ◻
‾‾‾
◻

⑥ A 🍭 costs 7¢. Cam buys a 🍭 . How much has Cam left?

◻ – ◻ = ◻

Cam has ◻ ¢ left.

◻
– ◻
‾‾‾
◻

See how many pizzas Mrs Winter ordered for her class. Then answer the questions.

⑦ How many did Mrs Winter order? _____

⑧ How many were there in each pizza? _____

⑨ How many of pizzas were there in all? _____

⑩ There were 24 children in Mrs Winter's class. Each child ate 1 . How many were left? _____

⑪ 15 of the children were girls. How many were boys? _____ boys

⑫ **Start** At what time did the party start? _____

⑬ **End** At what time did the party end? _____

Look at the ribbons. Write the letters to answer the questions.

⑭ Which piece of ribbon is the longest?   Ribbon _____

⑮ Which piece of ribbon is the shortest?   Ribbon _____

⑯ Which piece of ribbon has the same length as
    3 ▭ ?   Ribbon _____

⑰ Which piece of ribbon has the same length as
    4 ▭ ?   Ribbon _____

Look at the number cards. Then circle the correct answers.

| 1 | 2 | 3 | 1 | 1 | 1 | 2 | 2 | 1 |

⑱ Is there a better chance that you will pick
    a **1** or a **2** ?   **1**   **2**

⑲ Is there a better chance that you will pick
    a **2** or a **3** ?   **2**   **3**

⑳ Which number card are you most likely
    to pick?   **1** **2** **3**

Look at the pictograph. Then circle the correct answers.

Favourite Snacks in Mrs Miller's Class

㉑ Which is the most popular snack?

㉒ Which is the least popular snack?

㉓ How many children like ?   5   6   7

㉔ How many children like ?   5   6   7

㉕ How many more children like
than ?   1   2   3

㉖ If 3 girls like , how many boys
like ?   2   3   4

See how many pets are in each shop. Then answer the questions.

	🐕	🐈	🐇
ABC PETSHOP	32	16	9
Bingo PET SHOP	14	28	13

㉗ How many pets are in ABC Pet Shop?

_____ = _____   _____ pets

㉘ How many pets are in Bingo Pet Shop?

_____ = _____   _____ pets

㉙ How many more dogs are in ABC Pet Shop than Bingo Pet Shop?

_____ = _____   _____ more dogs

㉚ How many more cats are in Bingo Pet Shop than in ABC Pet Shop?

_____ = _____   _____ more cats

㉛ How many rabbits are in both pet shops?

_____ = _____   _____ rabbits

㉜ How many cats are in both pet shops?

_____ = _____   _____ cats

㉝ If there are 13 white dogs in ABC Pet Shop, how many dogs in ABC Pet Shop are not white?

_____ = _____   _____ dogs

1. Comparing, Sorting and Ordering

↪ Children may have difficulty in recognizing positions such as left and right. Parents should give them more practice in various situations so that they can internalize the concept.

↪ Ordering is a higher level of comparing. Parents can let children arrange objects under various rules.

2. Numbers 1 to 10

↪ Through games and daily experiences, children can learn and understand the difference between cardinal numbers (1, 2, 3 ...) and ordinal numbers (1st, 2nd, 3rd ...).

Example   5 children are buying snacks. Mary is the first one in the line.

↪ Practising counting forward and backward helps children understand more about number sequencing.

↪ Simple words such as and/join (for addition), and take away/leave (for subtraction) can be used to guide children's calculation before they can use "+", "–" and "=" signs.

3. Addition and Subtraction

↪ To write vertical addition or subtraction, it is necessary to align all the numbers on the right-hand side.

Example   Vertical addition :

$$
\begin{array}{r}
3 \\
+\ 1 \\
\hline
4
\end{array}
$$ ⟋ align on the right-hand side

Matching addition sentence:
3 + 1 = 4

Vertical subtraction :

$$
\begin{array}{r}
5 \\
-\ 3 \\
\hline
2
\end{array}
$$ ⟋ align on the right-hand side

Matching subtraction sentence:
5 – 3 = 2

4. Numbers 11 to 20

↪ Counting on (forward) helps to find the sum faster.

Example   7 plus 5 means counting 5 forward from 7, and the sum of 7 + 5 is 12.

↪ Counting back (backward) helps to find the difference faster.

Example   13 minus 4 means counting 4 backward from 13, and the difference of 13 – 4 is 9.

↔ Any number plus or minus 0 equals itself.

Examples $7 + 0 = 7$ $9 - 0 = 9$

↔ Using tens may also help to find the sum or difference faster.

Examples $7 + 5 = 7 + 3 + 2$ $(5 = 3 + 2)$ $13 - 4 = 10 + 3 - 4$ $(13 = 10 + 3)$
                $= 10 + 2$ $= 10 - 4 + 3$ (order changed)
                $= 12$ $= 6 + 3$
                                                    $= 9$

↔ Even if the order of addition changes, the answer remains the same.

Example $5 + 4 = 4 + 5 = 9$

5.   Numbers 20 to 100

↔ It is easier for children to learn the numbers 20 to 100 by splitting them into two stages: 20 to 50, and 50 to 100

↔ Counting in groups of ten leads to the recognition of ones and tens.

Example

                                               2 tens and 4 ones
              2 tens $= 20 + 4$
                                            $= 24$

4 ones

↔ When comparing numbers, parents should remind children to compare the tens digit first, and if they are the same, compare the ones.

Examples   1.   Which one is greater, 25 or 51?
                  Compare the tens digit.

                        2|5
                        5|1
                 ∟ 5 is greater than 2

     51 is greater than 25.

         2.   Which one is greater, 38 or 32?

                 Compare the tens digit.   Compare the ones digit.

                          3|8   3|8|
                          3|2   3|2|
                   ∟ same   ∟ 8 is greater than 2

     38 is greater than 32.

6.   More about Addition and Subtraction

↔ Before doing addition and subtraction, parents should make sure that children understand the meaning of place value. Children should understand that the digits in a 2-digit number represent groups of tens and groups of ones respectively.

Example   Sixty-five can be written as 65, six tens and five ones, and 60 + 5.

↦ To do vertical addition or subtraction:

1st   Align the numbers on the right-hand side.
2nd Add or subtract the ones.
3rd   Add or subtract the tens.

Example   16 + 23 =

1st	2nd	3rd
1 6 + 2 3	1 6 + 2 3 9	1 6 + 2 3 3 9

↦ If the sum of the ones is 10, remind children to write 0 under the ones column, and bring 1 to the tens column.

Example

$$\begin{array}{r} 1\;3 \\ +\;\;2\;7 \\ \hline 4 \end{array}$$ ✗ $$\begin{array}{r} 1\;3 \\ +\;\;2\;7 \\ \hline 4\;0 \end{array}$$ ✓

↦ If the difference of the ones is 0, remind children to write 0 under the ones column.

Example

$$\begin{array}{r} 3\;2 \\ -\;\;1\;2 \\ \hline 2 \end{array}$$ ✗ $$\begin{array}{r} 3\;2 \\ -\;\;1\;2 \\ \hline 2\;0 \end{array}$$ ✓

↦ If the difference of the tens is 0, there is no need to write 0 under the tens column.

Example

$$\begin{array}{r} 3\;8 \\ -\;\;3\;0 \\ \hline 0\;8 \end{array}$$ ✗ $$\begin{array}{r} 3\;8 \\ -\;\;3\;0 \\ \hline 8 \end{array}$$ ✓

7. Measurement

↦ Parents should encourage children to describe dimensions with mathematical language, e.g. height, length, width etc., and use appropriate non-standard units such as erasers or books to measure different things. After that, parents can show them how to use standard units, e.g. centimetres, to do measurement.

↦ To measure the length of an object, remind children to align "0" to one end of the object and get the length of the object from the other end.

Example

The pencil is 8 cm long. ✗   The pencil is 7 cm long. ✓

8. Time

- ➡ Children learn how to read the analog clock and tell the time by the hour and half hour. As they may have difficulty telling the exact position of the hour hand, parents should provide more guidance and practice for them.

  Example

half-past three ✗

The hour hand is halfway between 3 and 4.

half-past three ✓

9. Money

- ➡ Children learn to name coins up to $2 and state the value of pennies, nickels and dimes. Real coins can be used to play "buying things" with children to get them familiar with the value of each coin.

10. Shapes

- ➡ At this stage, children learn to recognize some 3-dimensional figures such as sphere, cylinder, cube and cone, and some 2-dimensional figures such as circle, triangle, square, and rectangle. Parents may let children use building blocks and construction sets to consolidate their concepts of 3-dimensional and 2-dimensional figures.

- ➡ Symmetrical figures may have more than 1 line of symmetry.

  Example

This symmetrical figure has 2 lines of symmetry.

11. Graphs

- ➡ Children need to know how to display and interpret data in a pictograph or solid column graph. Parents should encourage them to make comments about the graphs so that they can develop a better understanding of the data shown in the graphs.

ANSWERS – SECTION 1

1 Comparing Sizes

7- 9. (Suggested answers)

13 - 15. (Suggested answers)

25 - 27.

28. smaller	29. bigger	30. bigger
31. bigger	32. smaller	33. bigger
34. smallest	35. biggest	

2 Comparing Heights and Lengths

7- 12. (Suggested answers)

COMPLETE MATHSMART (GRADE 1)   **249**

3 Comparing Shapes and Weights

1.
2.
3.
4.
5.
6.
7.
8.
9.
10.

11. 12. 13.
14. A   15. C   16. C
17. 18. 19. 20.
21. heavier   22. lighter   23. heavier
24. heavier   25. heavy   26. lighter

4 Comparing Positions

1. under   2. on   3. right
4. left   5. right   6. behind
7. in front of   8. inside   9. outside
10. right   11. left   12. right
13. right   14. in front of   15. behind
16. behind   17. over   18. under
19. over   20. under

21-22.   23. inside
24-25.   26. over
27-28.   29. behind

30 – 39. (Suggested answers)
30 – 33.   34 - 36.
37 –39.

5 Matching and Arranging Objects

1. oranges
2. pears
3. apples or oranges or peaches
4. peaches
5.   6.
7. or   8. or
9.   10.   11.
12. fewer   13. more   14. fewer
15. C ; D ; A ; B   16. D ; B ; C ; A   17. D ; B ; A ; C ; E
18. D ; C ; A ; B ; E
19. bigger   20. bigger   21. B
22. C   23. B ; A ; C
24 – 25. (Suggested answers)
24.   25.

Midway Review

1a. red, yellow

b. B ; C ; D ; A

2a.   blue, green

b. D ; C ; A ; B

3 – 6. (Suggested answers)

7. in front of 8. right 9. left
10. under 11. inside 12. bigger
13. more 14. A 15. B
16. B 17. A 18. right
19. left 20. left 21. behind
22. over 23. outside 24. inside
25. B 26. A 27. A
28. A
29.

30. B 31. C 32. B ; A ; C

6 Ordering Objects (1)

5.
6.
7. 8.
9. 10.

11. D ; C ; B ; A 12. D ; C ; B ; A

7 Ordering Objects (2)

1. A ; C ; D ; B 2. B ; A ; C ; D 3. B ; A ; C ; D
4. B ; D ; A ; C 5. D ; A ; B ; C 6. C ; D ; B ; A
7. B ; A ; D ; C 8. C ; B ; A ; D 9. A ; D ; C ; B
10. C ; A ; D ; B 11. B 12. A
13. B 14. C 15. C
16. C ; A ; B 17. B ; C ; A

18.

19. Bert 20. Adam
21. Bert ; Dan ; Adam 22. Dan
23. Adam 24. Dan
25. Adam 26. Dan ; Bert ; Adam

8 Sorting Objects (1)

5.

6.

7.

8.

9.

10.

11.

12.

13.

14.

15.

16.

17.

18.

19.

20.

21.

22.

23.

9   Sorting Objects (2)

1.

2.

3.

4.

5.

6.

7.

8.

9. can fly : B ; D   cannot fly : A ; C ; E
10. edible : A ; C ; D   not edible : B ; E
11. stationery : C ; D   not stationery : A ; B ; E
12. toys : B ; E   not toys : A ; C ; D
13. animals : B ; C ; E   plants : A ; D

14.

15.

16.

Final Review

1.

2.

3.

4.

5.

7b. B ; A ; C

11. B ; C ; A   12. A ; B ; C
13. A ; C ; B   14. C ; B ; A

1   Addition and Subtraction of 1

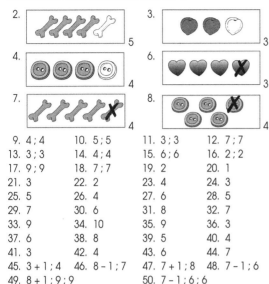

2. (5)
3. (3)
4. (4)
6. (3)
7. (4)
8. (4)

9. 4 ; 4	10. 5 ; 5	11. 3 ; 3	12. 7 ; 7
13. 3 ; 3	14. 4 ; 4	15. 6 ; 6	16. 2 ; 2
17. 9 ; 9	18. 7 ; 7	19. 2	20. 1
21. 3	22. 2	23. 4	24. 3
25. 5	26. 4	27. 6	28. 5
29. 7	30. 6	31. 8	32. 7
33. 9	34. 10	35. 9	36. 3
37. 6	38. 8	39. 5	40. 4
41. 3	42. 4	43. 6	44. 7

45. 3 + 1 ; 4   46. 8 − 1 ; 7   47. 7 + 1 ; 8   48. 7 − 1 ; 6
49. 8 + 1 ; 9 ; 9   50. 7 − 1 ; 6 ; 6
51. 6 − 1 ; 5 ; 5

Just for Fun

3 ; 4 ; 6 ; 7 ; 8 ; 10 ; 11 ; 12 ; 13 ; 15 ; 16 ; 17 ; 18 ; 19

2   Addition Facts to 6

2. 3 , 3 ; 6	3. 3 , 2 ; 5	4. 4 , 2 ; 6	5. 2 , 2 ; 4
6. 1 , 5 ; 6	7. 1 , 4 ; 5	8. 2 , 2 ; 4	9. 6
10. 5	11. 5	12. 3	13. 6
14. 4	15. 5	16. 6	17. 6
18. 2	19. 4	20. 5	21. 6
22. 4	23. 6	24. 6	25. 4
26. 3	27. 5	28. 6	29. 5
30. 5	31. 3	32. 6	33. 6
34. 4		35. 2 + 3 ; 3 + 2 ; 4 + 1	

36. 1 + 5 ; 3 + 3 ; 2 + 4 ; 5 + 1

37. ○○ ○○○ ○○○○ → (flower)
    2 , 4 ; 6

38. ○○ ○○○ ○○○○ → (flower)
    2 , 3 ; 5

39. 3 , 2 ; 5 ; 5   40. 4 , 2 ; 6 ; 6   41. 3 , 3 ; 6 ; 6

Just for Fun

2 + 3   1 + 3   2 + 4   2 + 1

2 + 2   4 + 1   1 + 2   3 + 3

3   Subtraction Facts to 6

2. 4 , 2 ; 2	3. 6 , 2 ; 4	4. 5 , 2 ; 3	5. 5 , 3 ; 2
6. 5 , 4 ; 1	7. 3 , 2 ; 1	8. 6 , 3 ; 3	
9. 2	10. 5	11. 1	12. 1
13. 2	14. 1	15. 4	16. 3
17. 1	18. 2	19. 3	20. 3
21. 4	22. 2	23. 1	24. 2
25. 4	26. 2	27. 2	28. 2
29. 1	30. 3	31. 1	32. 3
33. 4	34. 1		

35. 5 − 3 ; 4 − 2 ; 3 − 1   36. 5 − 4 ; 3 − 2 ; 6 − 5

 37. (cherries, bananas) 5 ; 3
 38. (bananas) 5 ; 2

39. 4 , 2 ; 2   40. 5 , 2 ; 3
41. 6 , 3 ; 3   42. 6 , 2 ; 4   43. 4 , 3 ; 1   44. 3 , 2 ; 1

Just for Fun

1   2   3   4

4 − 2   6 − 2   5 − 4   4 − 1

4   Addition and Subtraction of 0

1. 4	2. 0	3. 0	4. 3
5. 0	6. 4	7. 3	8. 5
9. 6	11. 6	12. 5	13. 5
14. 4	15. 4	16. 3	17. 3
18. 2	19. 2	20. 1	21. 1
22. 0	23. 0	24. 5	25. 4
26. 3	27. 1	28. 6	29. 3
30. 5	31. 6	32. 4	33. 2
34. 4	35. 2		

36.

37. 2 ; 6   38. 5 ; 3 ; 1
39. 1 ; 3 ; 5   40. 6 ; 2 ; 4
41. 4 ; 4   42. 3 + 0 = 3 ; 3
43. 4 − 0 = 4 ; 4   44. 6 − 0 = 6 ; 6

Just for Fun

5   Addition and Subtraction Facts to 6

2. 6 − 1 ; 5	3. 3 + 3 ; 6	4. 4 − 2 ; 2
5. 5 − 2 ; 3	6. 2 + 3 ; 5	

7. 1	8. 4	9. 4	10. 3
11. 6	12. 3	13. 6	14. 3
15. 0	16. 2	17. 2	18. 3
19. 4	20. 5	21. 5	22. 1
23. 4	24. 1	25. 5	26. 1
27. 1	28. 6	29. 2	30. 2
31. 2	32. 4	33. 6	34. 5
35. 3	36. 4	37. 6	38. 3
39. 3	40. 2	41. 6	42. 5
43. 3	44. 1	45. 2	46. 4

47. 2 ; 2   48. 4 + 2 = 6 ; 6
49. 3 + 3 = 6 ; 6   50. 6 − 4 = 2 ; 2
51. 5 − 2 = 3 ; 3   52. 5 − 1 = 4 ; 4

Just For Fun

6 Addition Facts to 10

1. 9
2. 7, 3 ; 10
3. 5, 4 ; 9
4. 8, 1 ; 9
5. 4, 4 ; 8
6. 4, 3 ; 7
7. 6, 4 ;10
8. 9
9. 10
10. 10
11. 9
12. 9
13. 10
14. 9
15. 10
16. 8
17. 8
18. 7
19. 7
20. 10
21. 8
22. 9
23. 10
24. 8
25. 9
26. 8
27. 8
28. 9
29. 10
30. 7
31. 9
32. 7
33. 7

35.
36.

6, 3   7, 2

37.
38.

8, 1   9, 0

39.
40.

4, 4   5, 3

41.
42.

6, 2   7, 1

43.
44.

8, 0   4, 3

45.
46.

5, 2   6, 1

47.

7, 0

48.
49.

50. 8, 0 ; 8 ; 8
51. 6, 4 ; 10 ; 10
52. 6, 3 ; 9 ; 9

Just for Fun

7 Subtraction Facts to 10

1. 6
2. 10, 2 ; 8
3. 9, 4 ; 5
4. 8, 2 ; 6
5. 8, 4 ; 4
6. 7, 3 ; 4
7. 8, 6 ; 2
8. 6
9. 6
10. 6
11. 2
12. 5
13. 5
14. 5
15. 1
16. 1
17. 2
18. 2
19. 4
20. 4
21. 3
22. 3
23. 1
24. 2
25. 4
26. 1
27. 2
28. 3
29. 5
30. 8
31. 4
32. 10
33. 8

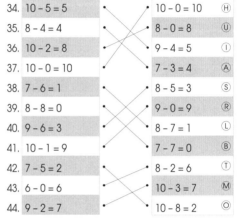

34. 10 – 5 = 5   10 – 0 = 10   H
35. 8 – 4 = 4   8 – 0 = 8   U
36. 10 – 2 = 8   9 – 4 = 5   I
37. 10 – 0 = 10   7 – 3 = 4   A
38. 7 – 6 = 1   8 – 5 = 3   S
39. 8 – 8 = 0   9 – 0 = 9   R
40. 9 – 6 = 3   8 – 7 = 1   L
41. 10 – 1 = 9   7 – 7 = 0   B
42. 7 – 5 = 2   8 – 2 = 6   T
43. 6 – 0 = 6   10 – 3 = 7   M
44. 9 – 2 = 7   10 – 8 = 2   O

45. BRITISH COLUMBIA

46.
47.

48. 7, 4 ; 3 ; 3
49. 8, 3 ; 5 ; 5
50. 10, 2 ; 8 ; 8

Just for Fun

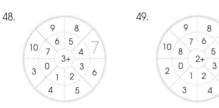

8 Addition and Subtraction Facts to 10

1. 9
2. 4 + 2 + 1 ; 7
3. 9 – 2 ; 7
4. 9 – 3 ; 6
5. 2 + 4 + 4 ; 10
6. 4 + 3 ; 7
7. 7
8. 2
9. 6
10. 10
11. 9
12. 3
13. 2
14. 7
15. 10
16. 1
17. 7
18. 7
19. 9
20. 10
21. 8
22. 9
23. 9
24. 8
25. 1
26. 3
27. 2
28. 5
29. 7
30. 8
31. 10
32. 9
33. 4
34. 9
35. 3
36. 10
37. 5
38. 2
39. 10
40. 10
41. 6
42. 4
43. 9
44. 6
45. 8
46. 5
47. 5
48. 4
49. 10
50. 3
51. 7
52. 6 ; 6
53. 10
54. 9

```
   6              5
 + 4            + 4
 ---            ---
  10              9
```

55.
```
3        9
      -  6
         3
```

56. 7
```
         2
         4
      +  1
         7
```

Just for Fun
3 ; 4

Midway Review

1. 9 – 3 ; 6　　2. 5 + 3 + 1 ; 9　　3. 6 + 4 ; 10
4. 5　　5. 6　　6. 2　　7. 2
8. 7　　9. 1　　10. 6　　11. 7
12. 9　　13. 7　　14. 9　　15. 1
16. 3　　17. 8　　18. 2　　19. 7
20. 4　　21. 8

22.
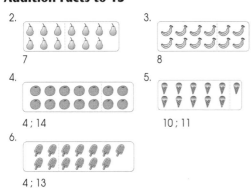

23.

24.

25.

26.

27. 10 ; 8　　28. 4 ; 0 ; 2　　29. –　　30. +
31. 5　　32. 2　　33. 4　　34. 3
35. 3　　36. 4　　37. 2　　38. 5
39. –　　40. +　　41. +　　42. –
43. –　　44. +　　45. –　　46. +
47. –　　48. –　　49. +　　50. +
51. 1　　52. 3　　53. 4　　54. 4
55. 4　　56. 3

57. 8
```
        10
      -  2
         8
```
58. 3
```
         6
      -  3
         3
```
59. 9
```
         5
      +  4
         9
```

60. 8
```
         2
      +  6
         8
```
61. 7
```
         4
      +  3
         7
```
62. 4
```
         8
      -  4
         4
```

9　Addition Facts to 15

2.

7

3.

8

4.

4 ; 14

5.

10 ; 11

6.

4 ; 13

7. 15　　8. 13　　9. 14　　10. 15
11. 14　　12. 12　　13. 12　　14. 13
15. 14　　16. 11　　17. 11　　18. 11
19. 14　　20. 15　　21. 13　　22. 15
23. 12　　24. 11　　25. 12　　26. 14
27. 13　　28. 14　　29. 15　　30. 15
31. 15　　32. 14　　33. 11　　34. 6
35. 10　　36. 5　　37. 9　　38. 4
39. 8　　40. 3　　41. 7　　42. 2

43.

44.

45.

46.

47. 14 ; 14
48. 13
```
        10
      +  3
        13
```
49. 12
```
        12
      +  0
        12
```

50. 11
```
         4
      +  7
        11
```

Just for Fun
5 ; 1

10　Subtraction Facts to 15

1. 8
2.
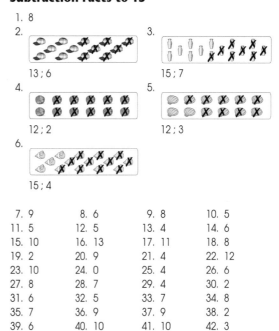

13 ; 6

3.

15 ; 7

4.

12 ; 2

5.

12 ; 3

6.

15 ; 4

7. 9　　8. 6　　9. 8　　10. 5
11. 5　　12. 5　　13. 4　　14. 6
15. 10　　16. 13　　17. 11　　18. 8
19. 2　　20. 9　　21. 4　　22. 12
23. 10　　24. 0　　25. 4　　26. 6
27. 8　　28. 7　　29. 4　　30. 2
31. 6　　32. 5　　33. 7　　34. 8
35. 7　　36. 9　　37. 9　　38. 2
39. 6　　40. 10　　41. 10　　42. 3
43. 9

44. 6 ; 6

45. 5
```
    12
  -  7
     5
```

46. 8
```
    13
  -  5
     8
```

47. 9
```
    15
  -  6
     9
```

Just for Fun

11 Addition and Subtraction Facts to 15

1. 9

3.

8

4.
13 ; 8

5.
12 ; 4

6.
4

7. 6	8. 13	9. 14	10. 4
11. 15	12. 6	13. 8	14. 11
15. 6	16. 14	17. 1	18. 15
19. 15	20. 9	21. 13	22. 5
23. 13	24. 2	25. 3	26. 7
27. 2	28. 15	29. 3	30. 14
31. 12	32. 6		

33.

+	4	5	6
7	11	12	13
8	12	13	14
9	13	14	15

34.

13	14	15	–
6	7	8	7
5	6	7	8
4	5	6	9

35.

36.

37.

38. 14 ; 14

39. 4
```
    13
  -  9
     4
```

40. 4
```
    14
  - 10
     4
```

41. 11
```
     5
  +  6
    11
```

Just for Fun

12 Addition Facts to 20

1. 9 , 8 ; 17	2. 14 , 5 ; 19	3. 11 , 6 ; 17	
4. 15 , 3 ; 18	5. 13 , 7 ; 20	6. 10 , 6 ; 16	
7. 20	8. 19	9. 19	10. 19
11. 19	12. 20	13. 19	14. 18
15. 17	16. 20	17. 17	18. 17
19. 17	20. 20	21. 19	22. 18
23. 20	24. 18	25. 16	26. 19
27. 17	28. 19	29. 20	30. 16
31. 20	32. 20		

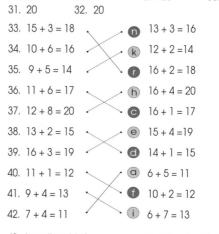

33. 15 + 3 = 18
34. 10 + 6 = 16
35. 9 + 5 = 14
36. 11 + 6 = 17
37. 12 + 8 = 20
38. 13 + 2 = 15
39. 16 + 3 = 19
40. 11 + 1 = 12
41. 9 + 4 = 13
42. 7 + 4 = 11

ⓝ 13 + 3 = 16
ⓚ 12 + 2 = 14
ⓡ 16 + 2 = 18
ⓗ 16 + 4 = 20
ⓒ 16 + 1 = 17
ⓔ 15 + 4 = 19
ⓓ 14 + 1 = 15
ⓐ 6 + 5 = 11
ⓕ 10 + 2 = 12
ⓘ 6 + 7 = 13

43. handkerchief
44. 10 + 10 ; 20 ; 20
45. 12 + 6 ; 18 ; 18
46. 8 + 8 ; 16 ; 16
47. 9 + 10 ; 19 ; 19
48. 13 + 4 ; 17 ; 17

Just for Fun

13 Subtraction Facts to 20

1. 8	2. 18 , 9 ; 9	3. 17 , 6 ; 11	
4. 19 , 7 ; 12	5. 20 , 10 ; 10	6. 19 , 9 ; 10	
7. 11	8. 7	9. 9	10. 15
11. 9	12. 6	13. 12	14. 14
15. 2	16. 13	17. 18	18. 3
19. 14	20. 6	21. 16	22. 6
23. 10	24. 12	25. 15	26. 9
27. 7	28. 6	29. 3	30. 4
31. 14	32. 13	33. 6	34. 7
35. 11	36. 5	37. 5	38. 1
39. 2	40. 5	41. 2	42. 7
43. 9	44. 12		

45. 18 – 12 ; 6 ; 6
46. 17 – 9 ; 8 ; 8
47. 20 – 18 ; 2 ; 2
48. 16 – 5 ; 11 ; 11
49. 19 – 9 ; 10 ; 10

Just for Fun

18 – 4   12 – 8   16 – 11
19 – 5   17 – 4   20 – 6   14 – 10

14 Addition and Subtraction Facts to 20

3. 7 ; 19
4. 18 ; 13

5. 20 ; 6
6. 9 ; 17

7. 14	8. 19	9. 19	10. 7
11. 3	12. 12	13. 3	14. 19
15. 4	16. 20	17. 20	18. 7
19. 20	20. 8	21. 17	22. 7
23. 20	24. 11	25. 3	26. 20
27. 4	28. 10	29. 16	30. 12
31. 20	32. 18		

33. 🏠 19 | 12 + 7 | 20 - 1 | 14 + 4 | 13 + 6

34. 🏠 16 | 20 - 4 | 12 + 3 | 19 - 3 | 9 + 7

35. 🏠 13 | 9 + 5 | 19 - 6 | 17 - 4 | 7 + 6

36. 🏠 15 | 18 - 3 | 9 + 7 | 17 - 2 | 11 + 4

37. 🏠 18 | 18 - 0 | 20 - 2 | 10 + 8 | 12 + 5

38. 🏠 11 | 16 - 4 | 7 + 4 | 17 - 6 | 9 + 2

39. 🏠 12 | 8 + 4 | 19 - 7 | 6 + 5 | 16 - 4

40. 5 ; 5

41. 10
```
  18
 - 8
  10
```
42. 14
```
  20
 - 6
  14
```
43. 19
```
  13
 + 6
  19
```
44. 13
```
  16
 - 3
  13
```

Just for Fun

65 ; 56 ; 48 ; 32 ; 29 ; 12 ; 7

15 More Addition and Subtraction

1a. 15	b. 16	c. 17	d. 18
e. 19			
2a. 17	b. 18	c. 19	d. 20
3a. 11	b. 12	c. 13	d. 14
4a. 9	b. 8	c. 7	d. 6
e. 5			
5a. 7	b. 8	c. 9	d. 10
e. 11			
6. 12			

7. 5 ; 15   8. 3 ; 13

9. 4 ; 14   10. 7 ; 17

11. 5 ; 15

12. 8
13. 2 ; 8   14. 3 ; 7

15. 4 ; 6   16. 3 ; 7

17. 2 ; 8

| 18. 14 | 19. 12 | 20. 18 | 21. 15 |
| 22. 16 | 23. 17 | 24. 19 | 25. 15 |

Just for Fun

🟨 yellow
🟥 red

16 Addition and Subtraction with Money

2. 6¢   3. 7¢   4. 8¢

5.
6.
7.
8.

9. 2   10. 5 , 4 ; 1   11. 7 , 7 ; 0

12. 10 , 5 ; 5
13. 10 , 6 ; 4
14. 3
15. 10 , 6 ; 4
16. 6 , 4 ; 2
17. 7 , 2 ; 5
18. 5 , 5 ; 0
19. A
20. D
21. B , C
22. B , D
23. C , D
24. A , B

25.

26.

27.

28. 3¢ + 4¢ ; 7¢ ; 7
29. 6¢ – 4¢ ; 2¢ ; 2
30. 5¢ + 1¢ ; 6¢ ; 6
31. 5¢ – 3¢ ; 2¢ ; 2
32. 1¢ + 4¢ + 5¢ ; 10¢ ; 10

Just for Fun

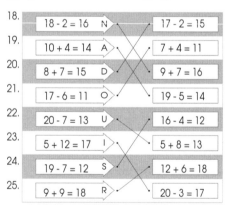

Final Review

1. 20
2. 11
3. 18
4. 15
5. 13
6. 16
7. 17
8. 10
9. 16
10. 10
11. 14
12. 19
13. 11 ; 8 ; 6 ; 9
14. 19 ; 18 ; 16 ; 20
15. 13 ; 10 ; 6 ; 12
16. 19
17. 13

18.–25.

18 - 2 = 16 N	17 - 2 = 15
10 + 4 = 14 A	7 + 4 = 11
8 + 7 = 15 D	9 + 7 = 16
17 - 6 = 11 O	19 - 5 = 14
20 - 7 = 13 U	16 - 4 = 12
5 + 12 = 17 I	5 + 8 = 13
19 - 7 = 12 S	12 + 6 = 18
9 + 9 = 18 R	20 - 3 = 17

26. DINOSAUR
27. +
28. –
29. –
30. +
31. +
32. –
33. +
34. +
35. –
36. +
37. –
38. –
39. 10
40. 5
41. 8
42. 2
43. 5
44. 1
45. 12
46. 3
47. 4th ; 1st ; 2nd ; 3rd
48a. 13
b. 14
c. 15
49a. 8
b. 9
c. 10
50. 3 ; 13
51. 3 ; 13

52. 3 ; 7
53. 4 ; 6

54.

55.

56. 12
$$\begin{array}{r} 18 \\ -\ \ 6 \\ \hline 12 \end{array}$$
57. 18
$$\begin{array}{r} 6 \\ +\ 12 \\ \hline 18 \end{array}$$

58. 5
$$\begin{array}{r} 10 \\ -\ \ 5 \\ \hline 5 \end{array}$$
59. 11
$$\begin{array}{r} 6 \\ +\ 5 \\ \hline 11 \end{array}$$

60. 6
$$\begin{array}{r} 15 \\ -\ \ 9 \\ \hline 6 \end{array}$$
61. 2
$$\begin{array}{r} 9 \\ -\ 7 \\ \hline 2 \end{array}$$

1 Comparing, Sorting and Ordering

1. B, A 2. A, B 3. B, A
4. B, A 5. A, B 6. B, A
7. in front of 8. left
9. inside 10. under
11. B 12. A 13. A
14. C

15. 16.

17. 18.

19. 20.

21. ✓ 🍎 ☐ 🍌
22. ☐ 🍎 ✓
23. ✓ 🐟 ☐ 🦐
24. ☐ 🍾 ✓

25. 1, 3, 2 26. 2, 3, 1
27. 2, 1, 3 28. 3, 1, 2

Activity

blue, green, brown, yellow

2 Numbers 1 - 10

1. 5 2. 6 3. 8
4. 7
5.
6. yellow

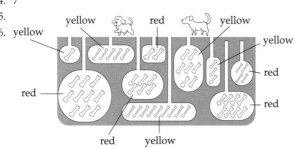

yellow, red, yellow, yellow, red, red, red, yellow, red

7. 5, 4, 3 8. 7, 8, 9
9. 9, 8, 7, 6, 5, 4, 3, 2
10.
11.
12.

13. 8 14. 3, 2, 5 15. 4, 2, 6
16. 5, 2, 7 17. 4, 5, 9 18. 3, 3, 6
19. 5, 1, 4 20. 8, 2, 6 21. 7, 2, 5
22. 8, 4, 4

Activity

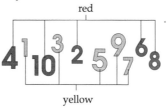

red, yellow

3 Addition and Subtraction

1. 5 2. 4 + 3 = 7 3. 5 + 2 = 7
4. 6 5. 8 6. 9
7. 7 8. 7 9. 9
10. 10 11. 10 12. 10
13. 10 14. 10 15. 10
16. 7 17. 8 18. 6
19. 7 20. 9 21. 8
22. 10 23.

4+2 2+3 3+4+1 2+1+3

24. 3 25. 2, 3 26. 2
27. 8, 2 28. 3, 3 29. 1
30. 3 31. 4 32. 4
33. 1 34. 8 35. 4
36. 5 37. 6 38. 5
39. 7 40. 4 41. 2
42. 7 43. 4 44. 6
45. 4 46. 4

Activity

6 and 4 3 and 7
9 and 1 2 and 8

4 Numbers 11 - 20

1. 12, even 2. 17, odd 3. 13, odd
4. 16, even
5. 11, 13, 15, 17, 19 6. 14, 16, 18, 20
7. 12, 13, 14, 15, 16, 17 8. 19, 18, 17, 16, 15, 14
9. 18, 16, 14, 12, 10, 8 10. 7, 9, 11, 13, 15, 17

11. ○ ○ ✓
12. ○ ✓ ○
13. ○ ○ ✓

14.   15 = 10 + 5

15.   15 = 12 + 3

16.   15 = 8 + 7

17.   17 = 6 + 11

18.   17 = 8 + 9

19.   17 = 10 + 7

20.   17 = 4 + 13

21. 8 + 8 = 16
```
    8
+   8
   16
```

22. 12 + 3 = 15
```
   12
+   3
   15
```

23. 11 + 0 = 11
```
   11
+   0
   11
```

24. 4 + 11 = 15
```
    4
+  11
   15
```

25. 13 + 0 = 13
```
   13
+   0
   13
```

26. 16 - 13 = 3
```
   16
-  13
    3
```

27. 15 - 9 = 6
```
   15
-   9
    6
```

28. 11 - 11 = 0
```
   11
-  11
    0
```

29. 13 - 3 = 10
```
   13
-   3
   10
```

30. 16 - 5 = 11
```
   16
-   5
   11
```

31. 4   32. 2   33. 8
34. 4   35. 1   36. 2

Activity
1. 2   2. 7   3. 1
4. 14   5. 11   6. 6

5   Shapes
1. A   2. D   3. C
4. B   5. E

6. Pyramid ☐   Sphere ✓   Prism ☐

7. Cylinder ☐   Prism ✓   Cone ☐

8. Cone ☐   Sphere ☐   Cylinder ✓

9. Cylinder ☐   Cone ☐   Pyramid ✓

10. Sphere ☐   Cone ✓   Cylinder ☐

11.
orange, blue

12.
red, purple, yellow

Activity

1.   2.   3.   4.

6   Solid Column Graphs
1. 7   2. 9   3.
4. 2
5.

6. 6   7. 5   8. Black
9. 1   10. Mrs Lee   11. Mrs Stanley
12. 2 squares   13. 1 square   14. 5
15. 5   16. 4   17. 14
18. Mark   19. David, 1   20. David
21. 4   22. 3   23. Jill
24. Mark   25. David, Nancy   26. 12

Activity
1.

2. 3   3. 5   4. 8
5. 2

7   Numbers 20 - 100

1. 71, 75, 77, 80, 82, 84, 86, 87, 90, 95, 96
2. 88   3. 76   4. 100, 92, 85, 73
5. 37, 39, 40, 42, 43   6. 26, 24, 23, 21, 20
7. 46, 47, 50, 51, 52   8. 91, 90, 89, 88, 86
9. 2 tens + 4 ones = 24   10. 3 tens + 8 ones = 38
11. 6 tens + 3 ones = 63   12. 7 tens + 4 ones = 74
13. fewer than 30, 22   14. fewer than 40, 34
15. fewer than 50, 45   16. more than 60, 62

17. 23, twenty-three

18. 30, thirty

19. 45, forty-five

20. 53, fifty-three

21. 30 + 5 = 35

22. 20 + 3 = 23

23. 60 + 0 = 60

24. 50 + 4 = 54

25.

Yellow			green		
30	44	62	21	37	49
	66	86		53	55	95

26. 3 tens and 6 ones = 30 + 6
27. 4 tens and 9 ones = 40 + 9
28. 6 tens and 1 ones = 60 + 1
29. 7 tens and 5 ones = 70 + 5
30. 9 tens and 0 ones = 90 + 0
31. 0 tens and 9 ones = 0 + 9
32. 15, 20, 25, 30, 35, 45, 50, 55, 60
33. 30, 40, 50, 60
34. by 10's
35. 10   36. 25   37. 40
38. 10, 20   39. 8, 40

Activity

Midway Test

1. B, A   2. B, A

3.   4.

5.   6.

7.

8.

9.

10.

11.

12. 3 + 2 = 5   13. 7 - 5 = 2
14. 3 + 2 + 3 = 8
15. 13   16. 0   17. 15
18. 9   19. 7   20. 8
21. 11   22. 14   23. 19
24. 14   25. 11   26. 0
27. 18   28. 6   29. 16
30. 15   31. C   32. B
33. D   34. E   35. A
36. C   37. D   38. E
39.

40. 3   41. 12   42. 7
43. 5   44. 19   45. B
46. A   47. B   48. B
49. A   50. B   51. B
52. A   53. A   54. A
55. 52, 50, 43, 40, 26, 17   56. 41, 36, 30, 29, 20, 15
57. 30   58. 60   59. 9

60. 0
61. 80
62. 10
63. 0
64. 80
65. 5
66. 9
67. 9
68. 5
69. 70, 80, 90
70. 80, 85, 90
71. 19, 21, 23
72. 50, 55, 60
73. 74, 76, 78
74. 60, 62, 64

8 More Addition and Subtraction

1. 43
$$\begin{array}{r} 32 \\ + \ 11 \\ \hline 43 \end{array}$$

2.
$$\begin{array}{r} 21 \\ + \ 46 \\ \hline 67 \end{array}$$

3.
$$\begin{array}{r} 8 \\ + \ 70 \\ \hline 78 \end{array}$$

4. 78
5. 79
6. 67
7. 59

8. 63, 63
$$\begin{array}{r} \overset{1}{3}4 \\ + \ 29 \\ \hline 63 \end{array}$$

9.
$$\begin{array}{r} \overset{1}{2}8 \\ + \ 56 \\ \hline 84 \end{array}$$
10.
$$\begin{array}{r} \overset{1}{3}7 \\ + \ 49 \\ \hline 86 \end{array}$$
11.
$$\begin{array}{r} \overset{1}{1}2 \\ + \ 78 \\ \hline 90 \end{array}$$

12. 64
13. 75
14. 36
15. 40

16. 73
$$\begin{array}{r} \overset{1}{3}3 \\ 25 \\ + \ 15 \\ \hline 73 \end{array}$$

17.
$$\begin{array}{r} \overset{1}{1}5 \\ 8 \\ + \ 23 \\ \hline 46 \end{array}$$
18.
$$\begin{array}{r} \overset{2}{1}6 \\ 19 \\ + \ 36 \\ \hline 71 \end{array}$$

19.
$$\begin{array}{r} \overset{1}{1}2 \\ 23 \\ + \ 27 \\ \hline 62 \end{array}$$
20.
$$\begin{array}{r} \overset{1}{3}2 \\ 7 \\ + \ 26 \\ \hline 65 \end{array}$$
21.
$$\begin{array}{r} \overset{2}{1}9 \\ 28 \\ + \ 19 \\ \hline 66 \end{array}$$

22.
$$\begin{array}{r} \overset{2}{1}6 \\ 27 \\ + \ 38 \\ \hline 81 \end{array}$$
23.
$$\begin{array}{r} \overset{2}{4}6 \\ 28 \\ + \ 9 \\ \hline 83 \end{array}$$
24.
$$\begin{array}{r} \overset{2}{3}7 \\ 27 \\ + \ 7 \\ \hline 71 \end{array}$$

25. 48 - 15 = 33
$$\begin{array}{r} 48 \\ - \ 15 \\ \hline 33 \end{array}$$

26. 68 - 22 = 46
$$\begin{array}{r} 68 \\ - \ 22 \\ \hline 46 \end{array}$$

27. 22
28. 42
29. 23
30. 15
31. 20
32. 17
33. 2
34. 0
35. 6
36. 0

37. 13 + 16 = 29
29
$$\begin{array}{r} 13 \\ + \ 16 \\ \hline 29 \end{array}$$

38. 36 + 21 + 16 = 73
73
$$\begin{array}{r} \overset{1}{3}6 \\ 21 \\ + \ 16 \\ \hline 73 \end{array}$$

39. 39 - 29 = 10
10
$$\begin{array}{r} 39 \\ - \ 29 \\ \hline 10 \end{array}$$

Activity

1. 44
2. 34
3. 56
4. 25
5. 47
6. 56
7. 25
8. 44
9. 34
10. 47
11.

9 Measurement

6. 4, 2
7. 6, 3
8. 8, 4
9. 10, 5
10. A
11. 5
12. 13

13.

14. 10   15. 18   16. A
17. B   18. A   19. B
20. Estimate: individual answer   Count: 28
21. Estimate: individual answer   Count: 15
22. Estimate: individual answer   Count: 40

23.

24.

25.

26.

27.

28.

29. 5   30. 15

Activity

green   yellow

10   Time

1. 5   2. 9   3. 12
4. 7   5. 6   6. 11

7.   8.   9.

10. A   11. B   12. B
13. A   14. Monday   15. Wednesday
16. Friday   17. Sunday   18. 7

19 - 22.

January	February	March	April	May	June
blue		green			red

July	August	September	October	November	December
red		yellow			blue

23. A   24. B   25. B
26. C   27. 3, 1, 2, 4

Activity

red   yellow   green

11   Money

Dime   25¢
Loonie   10¢
Quarter $1
Toonie   1¢
Nickel $2
Penny   5¢

7. 3   8. 2   9. 2
10. 2   11. 3   12. 1
13. B   14. B   15. A
16. B   17. A   18. A

19.
20.
21.
22.

23. 47   24. 35

25. 33   26. 32

27.

	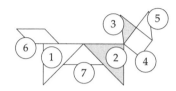			
28. POP 54¢	2			4
29. 57¢	2		1	2
30. 64¢	2	1		4

31. $\begin{array}{r} 2\,8 \\ +\ 2\,5 \\ \hline 5\,3 \end{array}$ 2

32. $\begin{array}{r} 4\,6 \\ +\ \ 5 \\ \hline 5\,1 \end{array}$ 9

33. $\begin{array}{r} 1\,8 \\ +\ 3\,7 \\ \hline 5\,5 \end{array}$ 5

Activity

1. 5   2. 50

12 Shapes

1. B   2. B   3. A

4. B   5. A

6. 3   7. 2   8. 5

9. 3   10. 1

11. Yes   12. No   13. Yes

14. No   15. Yes   16. Yes

17.   18.

19.   20.

21.   22.   23.

24. Square   25. Triangle

26. Rectangle   27. Hexagon

28.   29.   30.   31.

32.

Activity

1. 5

2. a.   b.

3. a

13 Pictographs

1. 8   2. 6   3. 4

4. 3   5. 2   6. 3

7. 21   8. 5

9.   10.   11.

12. 17   13. 30

14.

15. 1   16. 2   17. 10

18. 11   19. 19

20.

21. 6   22. 5   23.

24. 16

Activity

1. 4   2. 3   3. Summer

Final Test

1. 87	2. 41	3. 41
4. 82	5. 33	6. 60
7. 41	8. 22	9. 80
10. 31	11. 0	12. 20
13. 48	14. 76	

15. 39 + 0 + 25 = 64
64

$$\begin{array}{r} 39 \\ 0 \\ +\ 25 \\ \hline 64 \end{array}$$

16. 16 + 20 + 40 = 76
76

$$\begin{array}{r} 16 \\ 20 \\ +\ 40 \\ \hline 76 \end{array}$$

17. 43 + 28 + 0 = 71
71

$$\begin{array}{r} 43 \\ 28 \\ +\ 0 \\ \hline 71 \end{array}$$

18. 76 - 71 = 5
5

$$\begin{array}{r} 76 \\ -\ 71 \\ \hline 5 \end{array}$$

19.

20.
Shortest Longest

21.
Heaviest Lightest

22.
Thickest Thinnest

23.
Widest Narrowest

24. 8	25. 4	26. 3
27. 32	28. 8	29. 8

30.

31. 12   32. 2

33. Monday, Tuesday, Thursday

34. June, July

35 - 38.

Weather \ Season	Warmest	Coldest	Getting warmer	Getting colder
Spring			✓	
Summer	✓			
Fall				✓
Winter		✓		

39. 91   40. 82

41.

42 - 45.

	🪙	🪙	🪙	🪙
car 35¢	1	1		
top 40¢	1	1	1	
glasses 26¢	1			1
48¢	1	2		3

46. 47. E 48.

49. 50.

51.

52. a. 6   b. 4   c. 3
    d. 8

53. a. hexagons
    b. circles
    c. squares, rectangles

ANSWERS – Section IV

1   Numbers 1 to 10

1. 8	2. 7	3. Helen
4. 10	5. 6	6. 7
7. Dan	8. Rick	9. 8
10. 9	11. 7	12. 5
13. 8	14. 6	15. 6
16. 2	17. 8	18. Jamie
19. Barry		

2   Addition and Subtraction to 10

1. 3	2. 6	3. 9
4. 4	5. Carol ; Ann	6. 9
7. 10	8. 7	9. 6
10. 3	11. 5	12. 7
13. 3	14. 4	15. 3
16. 9	17. 3	18. 2
19. 9	20. 1	21. 6
22. 10	23. 7	24. 10
25. 2	26. 4	27. 3
28. 10	29. 6	30. 7
31. 2	32. 5	33. 2
34. 7	35. 2	36. 4
37. 7		

3   Addition and Subtraction to 20

1. 12	2. 16	3. 15
4. 9	5. 7	6. 13
7. 13	8. 11	9. 6
10. 8	11. 12	12. 14 ; 14

13. 20 ;
$$\begin{array}{r} 8 \\ +12 \\ \hline 20 \end{array}$$
14. 6 ;
$$\begin{array}{r} 12 \\ -6 \\ \hline 6 \end{array}$$
15. 4 ;
$$\begin{array}{r} 12 \\ -8 \\ \hline 4 \end{array}$$
16. 7 ;
$$\begin{array}{r} 12 \\ -5 \\ \hline 7 \end{array}$$

17. 18 ; 18
18. 11 − 7 = 4 ; 4
19. 17 − 5 = 12 ; 12
20. 12 − 5 = 7 ; 7
21. 13 + 7 = 20 ; 20
22. 13 − 7 = 6 ; 6
23. 3 + 11 = 14 ; 14
24. 11 − 3 = 8 ; 8
25. 6 + 6 + 6 = 18 ; 18
26. 20 − 18 = 2 ; 2
27. 12 − 4 = 8 ; 8
28. 12 + 5 = 17 ; 17

4   Shapes

1.

2. cube	3. prism
4. cylinder ; ✔	5. pyramid
6. ✗	7. ✔
8. ✔	9. ✗
10. ✗	11. 8
12. 7	13. 10
14. A	15. 2
16. rectangle	17. square
18. circle	19. triangle
20. hexagon	21. oval
22. 4 ; 4	23. 4 ; 4
24. 6 ; 6	25. 3 ; 3

26 – 28. (Suggested answers)

26.   27.   28.

29.   30.

31.   32.

33.   34.

35. 16	36. 14
37. 8	38. 8

5   Solid Column Graphs

1. B	2. C	3. A
4. A	5. C	6. Karen
7. Kim	8. 7	9. 5
10. 8	11. 12	12. 3
13. 20	14. 12	15. 4
16. 1	17. 3	18. 7

268   Complete MathSmart (Grade 1)